Yellowstone
BEARS
In the Wild

Jim Halfpenny

BY JAMES C. HALFPENNY

PHOTOGRAPHY BY MICHAEL H. FRANCIS
FOREWORD BY KERRY A. GUNTHER,
Yellowstone Bear Management Biologist

ISBN 10: 1-931832-79-X

ISBN 13: 978-1-931832-79-3

ABOUT THE PHOTOGRAPHS:

There are no photographs of captive or game-farm animals in this book. All the photos were taken in the wild in Yellowstone National Park and the Greater Yellowstone Ecosystem.

RIVERBEND PUBLISHING
P.O. Box 5833
Helena, MT 59604
1-866-787-2363
www.riverbendpublishing.com

DEDICATION

For one who loves
To Diann Thompson for the bears we watched and the hugs we shared.

For three who share
To Jim Garry, who enthralls us with the magic of bears through myths.
To Ron Cisar, who thrills us with the music of bears and Yellowstone wilderness.
To Bob Landis, who mesmerizes us with the motion of bears through cinematography.

For a grizzly that thrilled, enthralled,
and mesmerized us all
To bear 264

BEAR 264

ACKNOWLEDGEMENTS

This book grew from the magic of bears and the hearts of bear watchers I have known along the trail. It is a product of the questions asked by my students and the answers found by all who watch bears. Some folks go way back, some folks contributed but a short discussion which led, in part, to the inspiration for this book. It would not have happened without the generosity of sharing by watchers, students, researchers, field companions, and, most importantly, friends

Forming the backbone of this book is the knowledge gained by the researchers and managers of the Yellowstone Ecosystem for without that foundation this book would never have happened. When a reader sees a fact in this book, it is somehow related to or derived from the efforts of personnel in Yellowstone National Park or the Interagency Grizzly Bear Study Team! It is important to note that in this book one biologist may report ideas or findings that are, in fact, the result of many researchers collaborating in the study of bears. I thank everyone who has contributed to the historical development of these ideas, concepts, and research, and I apologize if some names were not included in my abbreviated coverage of these topics. Many have helped to increase our knowledge of the bear and many have shared their stories with me.

This book is a tribute to the generous input of the following people: Elaine Anderson, Gene Ball, Joel Berger, Mark Biel, Norm Bishop, Steve Braun, Gary Brown, Mark Bruchino, Pam (Gontz) Cahill, Marc Catellier, Chris Cauble, Susan Chin, Ron Cisar, Glen Cole, Jim Cole, Charlie Craighead, Frank Craighead, John Craighead, Lance Craighead, Collette Daigle-Berg, Troy Davis, Dale Ditolla, Bev Doolittle, John Dunlap, Ron Felzer, Dixie Finley, Judy Knuth Folts, Marilyn French, Steve French, Brad Garfield, Jim Garry, Barry Gilbert, Veryl Goodnight, Jerry Green, Deb Guernsey, Kerry Gunther, Bill Hamblin, Marc Hanna, Dan Hartman, Cindy Hartman, Steve Herreo, Mark Johnson, Minette Johnson, Pride Johnson, Chuck Jonkel, Bob Landis, Kate Kendall, Mary Ann Kendal, Wayne Kendal, John Kerr, Dick Knight, PJ Kremer, Bob Landis, Klari Lea, Deb Lineweaver, Carter Mackley, Larry Marlow, Mark Matheny, David Mattson, Greg McDonald, Rick McIntyre, Tom McNamee, Steve Mealey, Mary Meagher, Kenny Midkiff, Ben Mikaelsen, Craig Miller, Barb Moore, Kerry Murphy, Chuck Neal, Gary Norris, Judy Norris, Roy Ozanne, Doug Peacock, Belinda Peck, Lance Peck, Harold Picton, Dave Price, Roy Renkin, Sanjay Pyare, Matt Reid, Dan Reinhart, George Robinson, Hillary Robison, Larry Roop, Drew Ross, Janet Ross, Toni Ruth, Michael Sanders, Bart Schleyer, Paul Schullery, Chris Servheen, Francis Singer, Doug Smith, Tom Smith, Dan Stahler, Charles Schwartz, George Stevenson, Jana Stevenson, Diana Tombeck, Nathan Varley, Lisette Waits, Tom Watson, Barb Wehrfritz, Tami Whittlesey, Louisa Wilcox, Jason Wilson, Travis Wyman, and Ed Zito.

My thanks to the following organizations who have helped me with Yellowstone bears: Great Bear Foundation, Teton Science School, Yellowstone Association Institute, YNP Bear Protection through Education, and Yellowstone Grizzly Foundation.

I also wish to thank my publisher, Chris Cauble, for all he has done to make this book possible.Others, including Jenny Broom, Tom Ellison, Klari Lea, John Rogers, and Lynn Rogers, provided help over the longer run and are equally appreciated. Special thanks to Marc Catellier and Tami Whittlesey for their efforts to make the book a success. Let me also thank those who, due to the frailty of my mind, I may have inadvertently failed to acknowledge.

Finally, my heartfelt "thank you" to my alpha partner, Diann Thompson, for her love and encouragement.

All ursophiles are good folks who have touched me briefly, even long ago. I wish I could have shared more time with them. To these friends, I say, *long may the winds blow, the snows fall, and bears growl. Let's keep Yellowstone wild!*

CONTENTS

FOREWORD

Although Yellowstone National Park (YNP) was originally established to protect the area's geysers, thermal features, and scenic wonders, bears quickly became one of the park's primary and most popular attractions. By the late 1880s park visitors were enjoying watching bears that gathered to feed on piles of garbage dumped behind the early park hotels. As early as 1910, black bears had learned to panhandle for food from tourists traveling the park's roads in horse-drawn wagons. When cars replaced horses and wagons, increasing numbers of people traveled the park's roads and delighted in hand feeding, photographing, and interacting with bears.

Increasing visitation resulted in more garbage in park dumps and the increasing popularity of viewing bears feeding at the dumps. Park management even encouraged this activity by providing log bleachers and interpretive rangers at some locations. Unfortunately, having large numbers of park visitors interacting with so many human-food-conditioned bears resulted in large numbers of incidents of bear-caused property damage and bear-inflicted human injuries.

To remedy the situation, YNP implemented a new Bear Management Program in 1970. As part of the new program, hand feeding of bears was strictly prohibited, garbage cans were bear-proofed, and the garbage dumps were closed. To the dismay of many park visitors, the era of panhandling black bears lining the roadsides and large aggregations of grizzly bears feeding at garbage dumps came to an end. After more than a decade without human food handouts and garbage, the bear population had declined significantly, bears were rarely observed from roads, and it appeared that bears would never again be considered symbols of the park. Although the bear population declined, the public's interest in bears never waned. The public scrutinized every bear management decision and many vociferously proclaimed their dislike of the new Bear Management Program.

Although the 1970 Bear Management Program definitely had some short-term negative consequences, most would consider the long-term effects an amazing success. Today, bear-caused property damage and bear-inflicted human injuries are rare occurrences, and the bear population in the park appears to have reached ecological carrying capacity. An additional and completely unexpected result is that bears, grizzly and black, are once again highly visible from park roads. YNP is once again considered a "bear park" where people come in large numbers to watch, photograph, appreciate, and enjoy bears. Unlike years past, park visitors are not watching bears eating hotdogs and Twinkies; the bears today are involved in natural activities: scavenging carcasses, preying on elk calves, fishing, grazing, digging roots, and mating. All within view of large numbers of delighted tourist with binoculars and spotting scopes. Besides the entertainment, educational, and economic value, roadside bear viewing has built public appreciation for bears and a constituency of people that want to protect bears and bear habitat.

Yellowstone bears have probably been scientifically studied longer than any other bear population, and by some very well respected bear biologists—Olaus Murie, John and Frank Craighead, Richard Knight, Dave Mattson, Chuck Schwartz, and Mark Haroldson. In *Yellowstone Bears in the Wild*, Jim Halfpenny compiles and summarizes the vast amount and most up-to-date technical bear research into a scientific yet easily readable book. Into the science the author blends interesting corroborative accounts from the people who spend considerable time studying and/or observing bears. Jim Halfpenny covers everything from bear behavior to food habits and the successes of past management to the new challenges faced by bear managers today.

As this book goes to press there is great controversy over how grizzly bears in the Greater Yellowstone Ecosystem (GYE) should be managed into the future. Most state, federal, and many private biologists believe the GYE grizzly bear population has recovered, that public land and wildlife managers have learned enough about managing bears to ensure a bear population well into the future, and that grizzlies can be removed from Threatened Species status. Many other biologists and bear advocates believe that potential future threats to habitat and to important bear foods are too great to take any chances. One thing is certain, both sides are passionate about bear conservation.

As the controversy rages, bears—the great generalist omnivores—continue to survive in areas where humans find them socially acceptable. Bears seem well equipped to adapt to most environmental changes; it is usually human-caused mortality that determines where they can and cannot persist. In the GYE, more than 85 percent of grizzly bear mortalities are human-caused. In *Yellowstone Bears in the Wild*, Jim Halfpenny makes a significant contribution toward the preservation of bears by promoting better understanding of bear behavior, ecology, population dynamics, and habitat use, as well as how humans and bears influence each other.

Kerry A. Gunther, *Bear Management Biologist*
Yellowstone National Park

PREFACE

TO SEE A BEAR

"Students from my bear class and I watched spellbound as the grizzly swept rapidly back and forth through the grass of Antelope Creek. The bear had learned that by loping through the grass it could often spook an elk calf out of hiding. It worked. A calf broke from cover but the bear was on it before it covered five strides. Today the sow's cubs would eat."
— FIELD NOTES, JUNE 20, 1994

My class was not alone. As the sun rose, every parking space on the road to Mount Washburn held several cars, each containing people watching for bears. Since my first encounter with a grizzly in Yellowstone National Park in 1971, the number of people seeking their own experiences with Yellowstone's bears has grown exponentially. Of course, for more than a century people had come to Yellowstone seeking bears. But prior to the 1970s, most bear experiences were with "marshmallow bears" – bears habituated to people and, even worse, conditioned to eat human food along the roads, at feeding sites, and at garbage dumps.

The 1970s began a new era for bears and wildlife conservation. Garbage dumps were closed, roadside feeding was banned, and bears were weaned from human foods. Times changed and a cadre of dedicated bear watchers grew. Under directions from the blue-ribbon panel appointed by the National Academy of Science, a new team of park bear biologists and managers took over the search for knowledge.

Ursophiles, or bear lovers by any name, migrate to the Greater Yellowstone Ecosystem to see wild bears. A treat for any bear watcher is a safe roadside encounter with a grizzly bear such as this young male eating new green shoots of spring vegetation.

I have watched bears, bear watchers, biologists, and resource managers, and I have seen the changes. At times it has been a struggle, but the bears have benefited. Grizzly numbers have gone up, black bears thrive, and visitors now gaze in wonder at roadside sightings of grizzly and black bears. Building on the base of data and knowledge developed by earlier researchers, scientists are now showering us with new knowledge about bears.

Forty-six years of watching bears has not quelled my curiosity about the great bruins. My fate has led me to the far corners of North America seeking black, spirit (Kermode), glacier (blue), interior grizzly, coastal grizzly, coastal brown, Kodiak brown, and polar bears. Because of the presence of bears, I chose to make my home at the north gate of Yellowstone National Park. This location allows me frequent access to bear encounters.

This book is an overview of the knowledge garnered by Yellowstone biologists and bear watchers, and, of course, some of their personal stories. I have collected much of the new science so that all may share in the excitement of better understanding bears and bear country. Here are answers to questions that I receive from students in my wildlife classes and from the public visiting Yellowstone, and here are the cumulative efforts of many people to learn about and manage bears, black and grizzly. Here, too, are extraordinary photographs so that all may share in the beauty and awe of bears.

Incidentally, I use the term "bear watchers" in the broadest sense to include the visitors on the roads, the photographers, the videographers, the amateur naturalists, the managers, and the scientists. We are all watchers. We are all concerned with the future of the bear.

INTRODUCTION

YELLOWSTONE'S BEARS THROUGH THE DECADES

In the early 1970s when the snow became too deep to guide hunters in the backcountry beyond Yellowstone National Park's southeast corner, I retreated to Jackson Hole, Wyoming. There I skinned and butchered wild game for the Jackson Hole Cold Storage owned by John Dunlap. For a young man, it was a posh place to work. Besides meat processing, John made ice cream, wild game and bison jerky, and had the distributorship for Michelob beer. When there were extra packages of jerky or nearly empty ice cream containers, they were sent home with employees. John also expected us to celebrate with successful hunters who brought game to the plant. A celebration included a free beer for all. On some days it became difficult to cut a straight line on the side of an elk.

It was about 1971, after I returned from Vietnam, when two brothers and their hunting companions arrived at the plant. Out came the beer. I found myself drinking with Frank and John Craighead, who I knew and admired from their National Geographic films about grizzly bears in Yellowstone. To me, they personified grizzly bear research.

I don't remember if they had their own game or were simply friends with the hunters, but for a brief time I was accepted into their circle. They smiled, they toasted, and they talked hunting. And, of course, they talked bears!

The Greater Yellowstone Ecosystem has long been a stronghold for bears in the Lower 48 states, and recent opinion surveys by John Duffield indicate that wildlife viewing is the number one reason visitors come to Yellowstone. For most visitors, this sight of a black bear swimming across the Yellowstone River would create a lifelong memory.

In May 1971 I visited the biologist's office in Yellowstone National Park to learn more about bears. There I met Glen Cole. He was another honored name among bear biologists. Cole was serious but open, receptive, and tolerant of my questions.

These three great men of science stoked my thirst for knowledge about bears. Their kindness to me reflected their respect for bears and fellow *ursophiles*, those who love bears.

In 1971 these men were locked in one of the greatest bear debates of all times: the closing of the garbage dumps in Yellowstone. Though on opposite sides of the debate, they shared a love for grizzly bears and had the bears' survival at the heart of their philosophies. Eventually their reports and recommendations set the stage for bear research and management as it is practiced today.

Yellowstone National Park forms the core of the Greater Yellowstone Ecosystem (GYE), an area of about 18 million acres including 13.6 million acres of public lands. The GYE is larger than New Hampshire, Massachusetts, and Vermont combined, and it is more than half the size of New York State. The GYE consists of Yellowstone and Grand Teton national parks, six national forests, two national wildlife refuges, and lands belonging to Native American tribes, the Bureau of Land Management, the Bureau of Reclamation, and the citizens of the states of Idaho, Montana, and Wyoming. It is low in human population and low in miles of roads. In short, the GYE is prime habitat for black and grizzly bears.

A overview of the histories of the black bear and grizzly bear in the GYE is necessary to place our current knowledge and management in perspective. For those interested in a more in-depth view of bear history, I recommend Paul Schullery's book, *The Bears of Yellowstone*.

Black bears were encountered when Europeans first began exploring North America, but grizzlies remained largely unknown until Lewis and Clark described their encounters with the great bear on their 1804-1806 expedition. At that time grizzlies graced much of the western two-thirds of North America, but by 1904 grizzlies had been eliminated from 98 percent of their historic range. Through the early 20th century their numbers fell even more. By contrast, the smaller, more adaptable black bear continued to survive over most of the North America.

The GYE was one of the grizzly bear's last strongholds, and the decades of the 1950s and 1960s represented a turning point in their history here. It was the beginning of bear research in the ecosystem. To the south of Yellowstone National Park, biologists Bray and Barnes worked primarily on black bears. To the north of Yellowstone, John and Frank Craighead worked on grizzlies. Within the park, injuries to humans by bears peaked, with bears often nipping the hands of tourists feeding marshmallows to them and with bears exploiting garbage sources and ransacking campgrounds.

The 1960s was the decade of change. In 1960 Yellowstone began efforts to return bears to foraging for natural food. Management plans restricted garbage and prohibited roadside feeding. In 1963 the National Academy of Science issued the Leopold Report that suggested a park policy of natural regulation. As a result, a program to limit the size of the park's elk herd was halted in 1967, and the park's garbage dumps began to be closed in 1968. This action pitted the Craigheads against Cole and the National Park Service, and the decade ended with a major public controversy about the proper management of grizzlies.

The 1970s was the decade of revolution in science and management. The time was critical. There were only six grizzly bear populations remaining in the lower 48 states. In 1971 the last garbage dump in the park's interior was closed; the Gardiner dump on the park's border was closed in 1978.

In 1973 the Interagency Grizzly Bear Study Team (IGBST) was formed, led by Dr. Richard Knight. To monitor the health of the GYE grizzly population, the team selected the annual number of adult female grizzlies with cubs-of-the-year as the population benchmark. In 1975 the Endangered Species Act became law and grizzlies were officially listed as threatened. Although more than 200 grizzlies in the GYE had died due to conflicts from bears seeking new food sources as the dumps were closed, by the end of the decade the bears were garbage free and dining on natural foods. By 1980 grizzly numbers in the GYE had bottomed out and the population began a slow but significant increase.

The 1980s was the decade of three positive trends: an increasing grizzly population, growing knowledge of a grizzly bear's diet, and

Radio collars such as this one on a grizzly bear provide important information to scientists and land managers. Newer models transmit data via satellites.

incipient cooperation between land and wildlife agencies. In 1980 sport hunting of grizzly bears was stopped in the Lower 48 states. The 1982 Recovery Plan defined the GYE Recovery Zone, an area where grizzly bears would be given priority. Research and monitoring defined the roles for trout, whitebark pine nuts, army cutworm moths, and ungulates in grizzly bear diets. The Interagency Grizzly Bear Committee was formed to coordinate bear-related activities among the host of federal and state agencies governing the GYE. The decade ended with recognition of the role that bear mortality (or perhaps more accurately, bear survivorship) meant in increasing the bear population. Acceptable mortality limits were set at no more than two female grizzly deaths per year and no more than four percent annual mortality of the total population.

The decade of the 1990s was marked by increasing numbers of grizzlies and their wider distribution. There were more grizzlies and more female grizzlies with cubs-of-the-year south of the park. Some grizzlies killed cattle and sheep, and agencies struggled with management solutions. A plant disease called blister rust attacked whitebark pine, and illegally introduced lake trout in Yellowstone Lake began reducing the numbers of cutthroat trout. The use of moth aggregation sites by grizzlies bottomed out early in the decade. A multi-year drought reduced green vegetation. Nonetheless, in 1998 the GYE grizzly population met all demographic recovery goals established by the Recovery Plan.

The decade of the 2000s is one of delisting, or removing the grizzly bear from the Endangered Species List. A Conservation Strategy has been developed by state and federal agencies to assure the continued survival of grizzlies after delisting, including requirements for no net loss of habitat in the GYE. Still, there are uncertainties. Bark beetles and global climate change are affecting whitebark pine trees. Whirling disease is killing cutthroat trout. Human development continues, with each new home, road, and ski area adding pressure on the ecosystem. Time will tell how the bears will fare, and all *ursophiles* need to remain vigilant on their behalf.

A brown color phase of the American black bear prowls a Yellowstone stream bank looking for food before hibernation.

I. YELLOWSTONE'S BEARS

FROM THE FIRST BEARS TO TODAY'S BEARS

Long before there were tourists, before there were cowboys, before there were Native Americans, bears were roaming in or near the Yellowstone area, but not the bears we recognize today.

In Eurasia bears had evolved into three subfamilies: Ursavinae, Tremarctinae, and Ursinae. Episodic migrations from Eurasia established all three lineages in the New World. Ursavine bears gave rise to the Ursine bears, but all Ursavine bears went extinct worldwide by three million years ago.

The first Tremarctine bear in North America was *Plionarctos*, arriving about seven million years ago. Unlike today's bears, *Plionarctos* and its derived relatives, *Arctodus* and *Tremarctos*, had feet that pointed forward, not inward, and their lower jaws included a second muscle attachment not found in Ursine bears.

During the Pleistocene Ice Age, the giant short-faced bear (*Arctodus simus*), perhaps the largest land mammalian carnivore ever to roam North America, imposed its might on giant bison, horses, and even mammoths. This bear was estimated to have weighed on average more than 1,300 pounds and may have reached a maximum weight of more than 2,000 pounds. Fossils of the giant short-faced bear have been found near the Yellowstone area.

The giant short-faced bear had long legs and its toes pointed forward. Both adaptations allowed the bear to gallop at great speeds.

Not whiskers but porcupine quills protrude from the lips of this grizzly. Most porcupine quills eventually fall out or become encased in hardened scar tissue, but sometimes they are deadly. As the animal moves, the quill's tiny, backward-pointing barbs can work the quill deeper into the animal. If a quill penetrates an important organ, it could cause death. DALE AND ELVA PAULSON

Some scientists have argued that this was the fastest, greatest predator of all, while others, citing the bear's teeth, believe the huge bruin was a vegetarian. My late colleague Dr. Elaine Anderson, bear paleontologist and co-author of *Pleistocene Mammals of North America*, summed it up by saying, "When you are that big, you eat anything you please, anytime you want. The giant was probably little different than recent bears in that it ate vegetation but dined on meat obtained through predation whenever possible."

Two other bears also roamed North America, the lesser short-faced bear (*Arctodus pristinus*) and the Florida cave bear (*Tremarctos floridanus*), but their fossils have been found only in eastern and southeastern North America, not near Yellowstone. All three species of Tremarctine bears evolved in the New World but none survive in North America today; their reign ended during the Ice Ages. Today, the spectacled bear of South America is the only Tremarctine bear in the world.

During the Ice Ages the development of the great ice sheets lowered the sea level and allowed the formation of the Bering Land Bridge between the Old World and the New World. Many species, including bears, crossed the exposed land from Asia to North America. Perhaps as long ago as 4.3 million years, the first Ursine bear arrived in North America, *Ursus minimus*, a small bear whose fossils have been found in Idaho not far from Yellowstone. *U. minimus* is known as "First Bear" because it was the earliest bear of the genus *Ursus*, the genus of the true bears we know today.

First Bear probably gave rise to the ancestors of the American black bear, *Ursus americanus*, in the Old World about 1.5 million years ago. Those ancestors also migrated over the Bering Land Bridge and by 8,000 years ago *Ursus americanus* had replaced the Florida cave bear and the lesser short-faced bear. Scientists speculate their extinctions were ecological replacements resulting from the American black bear being a better competitor.

On the heels of the American black bear came another bear of the genus *Ursus*, the brown bear/grizzly bear (*see sidebar on page 13*). At the height of the last ice advance perhaps 50,000 years ago, several populations of brown/grizzly bears occupied Beringia, the area of the Bering Land Bridge including the current state of Alaska. Near the end of the Ice Age, some grizzly bears moved south toward Yellowstone. Common dogma says brown bears reached the continent's interior by traveling through a land corridor between the central continental and western mountain ice sheets about 13,000 years ago, give or take 1,000 years. However, a fossil leg bone found by Greg McDonald in an Oregon cave suggests brown bears may have reached the southern areas of the continent 30,000 years ago by a route along the coast.

No matter when or by what route, the arrival of grizzly bears evidently sealed the fate of the giant short-faced bear. Perhaps it was the new competition and perhaps it was climate and habitat change, but the net effect was the extinction of the giant bear by the end of the Ice Age. From then on, only grizzly and black bears roamed North America, including the Yellowstone area.

When Europeans arrived on North America's east coast, they found one bear species, the American black bear. The grizzly (*Ursus horribilis*) remained hidden in the remoteness of the west, known only to the Native Americans. In 1540 Spanish explorer Coronado may have encountered the grizzly in his expedition into the New Mexico area, and in 1602 Sebastian Vizcaino, another Spanish explorer, reported bears feeding on a whale carcass on the California coast. Since black bears were not found in that area, Vizcaino must have seen grizzlies. In 1691 Henry Kelsey of the Hudson Bay Company in Canada reported a "silver hair'd" bear, perhaps a grizzly.

Not much more was known about grizzlies until the Lewis and Clark Expedition. Native Americans warned the expedition about the great "white bear" to the west, and on October 20, 1804, the expedition encountered the "white bear" for the first time. Lewis wrote in his journal: "Peter Crusat this day shot a white bear he wounded him, but being alarmed at the formidable appearance of the bear he left his tomahawk and gun; but shortly after returned and found that the bear had taken the opposite rout." Clark said of the bear, "I saw several fresh tracks of that animal double the Sise of the largest track I ever Saw."

Crusat's encounter occurred on the prairie near the present town of Mandan, North Dakota. Grizzlies from the Yellowstone area remained unseen until the expedition's return from the Pacific Coast. On July 16, 1806, on the northern edge of the Yellowstone ecosytem in today's Park County, Montana, Clark wrote: "Also two white or Grey Bear in the plains, one of them I chased on horse back about two miles to the rugid part of the plain where I was compelled to give up the chase." And so the first Yellowstone grizzly encountered by non-Native Americans proved its formidable power by outrunning a horse.

2. BEAR HISTORY IN THE DNA

Two species of bears live in the Greater Yellowstone Ecosystem: the black bear (*Ursus americanus*) and the grizzly bear (*Ursus arctos*). These bears reflect dramatic differences in population survival and distribution. Genetic research is beginning to reveal the complex histories of these differences.

Genetic research analyzes DNA, and DNA comes in two forms: nuclear DNA (abbreviated nDNA) and mitochondrial DNA (abbreviated mDNA). Both forms are found in cells. Nuclear DNA occurs in the cell nucleus and half of it comes from the mother, half

What was that "white bear" shot by Peter Crusat of the Lewis and Clark Expedition? Was it a grizzly bear or a brown bear? Is there a difference?

Long before North American explorers encountered the grizzly bear, a similar bear in Europe and Asia was called a "brown bear." Its scientific name was *Ursus arctos* and, technically, all North American grizzlies are "brown bears" belonging to the species *Ursus arctos*.

But the bear encountered by Lewis and Clark became known as the "grizzly" in reference to its silver-tipped or "grizzled" hairs. In 1815 George Ord even provided a scientific name for the grizzly, *Ursus horribilis*, thus setting the stage for a controversy which often rages today.

The name controversy was further complicated by an explosion of scientific names for North American brown/grizzly bears. As the continent was explored, early biologists were certain that slightly different colors, sizes, and shapes meant a different species, and they often proclaimed a new species name. By 1917 the great naturalist C. Hart Merriam reported 86 or 87 species and subspecies of grizzly bears and brown bears in North America.

Indeed, hunters and biologists did recognize that different forms of the bears were found on the islands and coastlines of Alaska than were found in the interior of the continent. In some places (mostly on Alaska's islands and coastal areas) the bears were commonly called brown bears, and in other places (mostly in Alaska's interior and in the Lower 48 and Canada) the bears were called grizzlies. While the names implied different species, the bears themselves did not see a difference. They could and did interbreed—often, regularly, and successfully—thereby eliminating a popular if imperfect criterion for separating species.

In 1963 Bjorn Kurten, paleontologist and mammalogist of Pleistocene and Recent mammals, examined more bear skulls than anyone ever before, and based on identifiable breaks in a series of skull measurements, he concluded there were only three subspecies of *Ursus arctos*: the interior grizzlies, *U. arctos horribilis* (the horrible bear); the coastal brown bears, *U. arctos dalli*; and the Kodiak Island (Alaska) brown bears, *U. arctos middendorffi*. This classification is useful for communicating about recognizably different "subspecies," but new DNA evidence shows hybridization between these subspecies and a blurring of lines in some areas. Future taxonomic research may result in new subspecies names.

It is correct to say that Crusat's bear was a grizzly, and it is correct to call all *Ursus arctos* bears in the interior of North America, grizzly bears. Just remember that grizzlies are a subset of the brown bears of the world and, as such, are also brown bears.

The shape of the face, the prominent shoulder hump, and the small rounded ears help identify this Yellowstone bear as a grizzly, the common name for brown bears in the interior of Alaska and Canada, and the Lower 48 states.

from the father. Mitochondrial DNA occurs in cellular organelles called mitochondria located outside of the cell nucleus. Mitochondria are present only in the eggs of the mother. Therefore, nDNA comes from both parents but mDNA comes only from the mother.

Laboratory analysis of genetic makeup is called DNA "fingerprinting," and the technique actually sprang from a discovery in Yellowstone National Park. Biological prospectors found a bacterium, *Thermus aquaticus*, that tolerated unusually high temperatures in the park's thermal areas. From this bacterium scientists isolated an enzyme that survived high temperatures, and this enzyme is central to all DNA analysis, including DNA fingerprinting.

DNA fingerprinting can identify individual bears, a helpful tool in population studies. It can also reveal the mother's lineage through the mDNA and information about both parental lineages through the nDNA.

DNA mutations can cause new lineages to develop. For example, a mother of lineage A might, because of a mutation, give birth to an offspring with a different genetic code, designated lineage B. Subsequent offspring of each bear would be traced back to either A or B.

The rate of DNA mutation serves as a molecular clock. The mDNA code mutates in bears at a rate of 2.8 percent per million years. If two bears today had genetic codes that differed by 5.6 percent, their lineages would have diverged two million years ago.

What does DNA analysis reveal about black and grizzly bears?

Geneticists Stephen Wooding, Ryk Ward, and Lisette Waits have identified 19 different female lineages of black bears in the Lower 48 states. These lineages can be broadly grouped into two clades (groups with similar genetic codes). Genetic differences suggest that the clades divided about 1.7 to 1.8 million years ago, or about the beginning of the Pleistocene Ice Age.

DNA fingerprinting found that black bears from clade A exist in all parts of the U.S., but bears from clade B exist only in Alaska, along the Pacific Coast, and in the Rocky Mountains. This geographic arrangement probably means that black bear populations became isolated from each other during glacial advances and then recolonized areas as the ice receded, with bears from clade A successfully recolonizing the entire U.S. The clades began mixing as bear populations expanded after the melting of the last continental ice sheet about 18,000 years ago. Although mixing has been found at several locations just north of the GYE, the genetic code of Yellowstone black bears is pure clade A.

Interestingly, only three to five maternal lineages are present in the western bears of clade A. This suggests that all western clade A black bears, including those in the Yellowstone ecosystem, may derive from as few as three to five mothers.

DNA also provides insights into grizzly bear distribution. Lisette Waits discovered, at most, four maternal lines in GYE grizzlies. The presence of only a few maternal lines indicates low genetic diversity, a significant implication for conservation. Do GYE grizzlies represent only a few genetic lines that managed to colonize south of the ice cap, or do GYE grizzlies represent what was left after settlers killed off other grizzlies? Are Yellowstone grizzlies native to the ecosystem or were they pushed into Yellowstone as the Great Plains were settled?

To answer these questions, Craig Miller examined mDNA from grizzly skins and skulls in old collections. He found 23 maternal lines south of the Canadian border. This proves that grizzlies had spread out and diversified before the arrival of Lewis and Clark. The subsequent slaughter of grizzlies eliminated 15 lineages, including distinct lineages on all sides of Yellowstone. The remaining eight maternal lines represent populations that still exist. Significantly, Miller found only three of the eight lineages in the GYE.

Two lines of genetic evidence prove that settlers did not drive grizzlies into Yellowstone but that grizzlies were already here. Both historical and modern specimens from Yellowstone belong to the same lineages, indicating continued presence in the area since before settlers arrived. Additionally, historical lineages in Colorado, New Mexico, Arizona, Utah, and southern Idaho are distinct from those in Yellowstone, showing that those lineages evolved elsewhere, probably in those regions.

Waits and Miller's research has important implications for bear conservation. For example, it may become necessary to augment the genetic base of bears in the GYE to prevent problems with inbreeding. This would require bringing in bears from other populations. The closest maternal lineage to GYE bears is found in the Northern Continental Divide Ecosystem (NCDE) in northern Montana and southern Canada. If bears from the NCDE are brought to the GYE, managers would need to carefully select maternal lines that are different enough to increase diversity and perhaps ward off genetic bottlenecks.

The same consideration would be necessary for black bears since only three or four black bear lineages occur in GYE.

Black bears in the Greater Yellowstone Ecosystem have received less scientific attention than grizzlies because of the need for research on threatened grizzly bears. However, black bears play an important role in the area's ecology. This black bear mother and cub recently fed on an elk carcass; note the elk hairs on the cub's head.

II. BIOLOGY & BEHAVIOR

1. SIZE AND SENSIBILITY
Size counts

My bear is bigger than your bear! Perhaps size is the most common topic for bear watchers. It is certainly a cause for bragging rights. Of course, bear size depends on where you are and who is telling the story. Famed naturalist Adolph Murie long ago noted that the biggest bears were always furthest away from any scales. In the Yellowstone area, bears are always biggest at the K-Bar Saloon in Gardiner.

Many people wonder if half-ton grizzlies roam the GYE. Paul Schullery, noted historian and above all *ursophile*, reported in *The Bears of Yellowstone* that on July 9, 1870, Bart Henderson shot a large grizzly near Cooke City. According to Bart's story, "We was attacked by an old boar bear. We soon killed him. He proved to be the largest ever killed in the mountains, weighing 960 pounds." Paul notes that we do not know how, or really if, the bear was weighed.

I am only going to consider bears that were actually weighed or had their weights carefully estimated by chest girth measurements—no stories, no tales, no matter how good.

The heaviest Yellowstone grizzly "with documentation" that I know of was killed in 1916 near Old Faithful by Arthur Young for an exhibit in the California Academy of Science in San Francisco. When weighed in sections, the animal totaled 916 pounds. Dr. Saxton Pope, who also shot at the bear, estimated that 10 percent of the bear's live weight may have been lost as blood and waste during

For a bear, size is important. An approaching male grizzly of this large size captures everyone's attention.

processing. If true, the bear weighed about 1,000 pounds. The bear was shot in May and reportedly had no fat left over after hibernation. How accurate were the scales in 1916? It should be noted that this bear was probably feeding at a garbage dump.

Then there is the legend of the Thousand Pound Bear named "Bruno" (grizzly number 14), studied by the Craighead brothers. The heaviest recorded weight for Bruno was 890 pounds when live-trapped on September 5. Since the brothers figured he would put on additional weight before hibernation, Bruno was nicknamed the Thousand Pound Bear, even though he wasn't.

The Craigheads also trapped Fidel (grizzly number 206), which weighed 800 pounds, No. 115 which weighed 660 pounds, No. 13 which weighed 645 pounds, and Ingemar (No. 12) which weighed 620 pounds. All were males. They also reported the average weight of grizzly bears contending for top leadership at the Trout Creek garbage dump was 575 pounds. All weights were taken in June or July. (In some accounts referring to the Craighead research there are reports of a 1,120 pound (or 500 kg) grizzly bear. I have not been able to find such a bear in any of their scientific articles.)

The garbage dumps, or human-made ecocenters, supplied extra food for bears feeding at the dumps and those bears were heavy. After the dumps closed and bears reverted to natural foods, their weights went down, both average weights and heaviest weights.

The heaviest post-garbage-dump grizzly was 714 pounds, with other grizzlies recorded at 634, 609, and 600 pounds. The 714-pound bear was 16 years old, which is interesting because there are some suggestions that male grizzlies may lose weight after about 11 years of age. However, it should be noted that this bear foraged at the Cooke City garbage dump just outside the park.

Recently a grizzly killed east of the park was rumored at 800 pounds. However, an official for the Wyoming Game and Fish

Department explained there was an error in the weighing procedure and the weight was probably between 600 and 700 pounds. In May 2005 Kevin Frey of the Montana Department of Fish, Wildlife and Parks weighed a road-killed adult male grizzly at 645 pounds.

Black bears weigh considerably less than grizzlies at the same stages in their lives. Less is known about their size in the GYE but two researchers, Bray and Barnes, reported black bears average weights as 33 pounds for cubs-of-the-year (COY), 83 pounds for yearlings, 143 pounds for adult females (ranging from 135 to 160

pounds), and 243 pounds for adult males (ranging from 210 to 315 pounds).

Weights and growth rates of bears are complex biological phenomena involving several highly variable factors including gender, age, season, food source, and year-to-year variability in food supply. All factors must be in synchronization for a record weight. With the closure of the dumps, fewer heavy bears will be observed and weights will probably never exceed those of Bruno. Bottom line: 1,000-pound grizzlies do not exist in the GYE.

Bear weights do tell us quite a bit about bear biology. Weights are seasonally dependent. In general, bears emerge from hibernation having metabolized most of their stored fat, so bears are at their lowest weights of the year. During hibernation, adult male grizzlies may lose 18 percent of their weight and adult females may lose more than 30 percent. Lactating females lose more weight than males. A 400-pound male may lose 70 pounds during the winter. Over the spring and summer bear weights steadily increase, and in the fall weight gain shifts into high gear as bears prepare for hibernation.

Emergence from winter dens is a time of stress because new plant growth does not provide adequate calories for grizzlies to gain weight. This period has been termed the "negative foraging period." Bear biologist Bonnie Blanchard reports that adult grizzlies actually lose weight after emergence but regain it by August. On the other hand, cubs-of-the-year and yearlings gain weight after emergence.

Weight gains from mid-summer to fall may be considerable. During the summer, subadult grizzlies may gain more than 30 percent of their final fall weight. From early July to fall, adult males on average gain 2.2 pounds per day and adult females gain 0.9 pounds per day. The greatest weight gain is by three-year old males which gain 2.9 pounds per day in September. Fast growing young black bears may put on 70 pounds from spring to fall.

Red, white, black and brown bears

From the Native Americans to Lewis and Clark to Yellowstone bear biologist Milton Skinner, one color of grizzly bears has stood out:

FACING PAGE: *A large black bear may weigh about 300 pounds, a little less than half the weight of a large grizzly bear.*

RIGHT: *The grizzly bear derives its name from the white, gray, or "grizzled" tips on its long hairs. By late fall the coat of the grizzly becomes "silver tipped" and fills out to provide warmth.*

the white bear. In his 1925 book, *Bears in the Yellowstone*, Skinner described the coloration as a "rippling sheen of silver, covering older grizzlies with a royal robe of wild, majestic beauty, the coat quivered and rippled in waves when the bear moved."

A special characteristic of grizzly hair accounts for different coloration. On most grizzlies, the guard hairs (the long, thick hairs that form the outer coat) have white or gray tips, giving rise to such names as "silvertip," "white bear," and "grizzly" (for a grizzled

HOW BIG IS THAT GRIZZLY?

When you see a family of grizzly bears, you can estimate the ages and sizes of the cubs traveling with their mothers. First, estimate age. COY are less than half the mother's height and can walk under her stomach. Yearlings are up to 75 percent of mom's height, that is, half way between her belly and her shoulders, and they retain the short facial features of youth. Two-year-olds are up to 85 percent of the mother's height and look like smaller replicas of their mother. Three-year-olds are 95 percent of mother's height and look just like her in all proportions.

To estimate grizzly bear weights and heights, I use the following guidelines. Note that growth rates slow down after three years of age, although males continue to grow faster and larger than females.

For weights, I use the 75/100-pound guideline. Both female and male COY are about 50 pounds but males grow faster than females. For females add 75 pounds for each succeeding year, so female yearlings are 125 pounds, two-year-olds are 200, and three-year-olds are 275 pounds. For males add 100 pounds per year, so male yearlings are 150 pounds, two-year-olds 250, and three-year-olds 350 pounds. Three-year-old males actually average 393 pounds.

To estimate height at the shoulders, I use a five-inch rule. The average shoulder height for female COY is 20 inches, so female yearlings are 25 inches and two-year-olds are 30. Then growth slows down so three-year-old females are 33 inches and adults are 37 inches. Males are a bit taller, so start with male COY at 22 inches, then add five inches per year so male yearlings are 27 inches and two-year-olds are 32; three-year-old males are 37 inches and adult males are 40 inches.

After emergence from the den, a two-year-old grizzly cub looks like a smaller version of its mother.

appearance). Occasionally, however, some grizzlies lack this characteristic and may be dark brown or black.

Young grizzlies are usually dark but may be reddish, blond, or brown with great variation in the degree and location on the body where silver tipping occurs. Young grizzlies commonly sport a light-colored or white yoke on their chests. Subadults often have dark stripes on their backs. Young mature grizzlies generally fall into one of four color patterns: grizzled, front-grizzled, back-grizzled, or dark. Young bears tend to show more gray in the fall.

Dick Knight, retired head of the IGBST, and colleagues described coat color patterns in detail. I have grouped their descriptions into four color phases.

The "silvertip bear" is the classic color with silver- or gold-tipped guard hairs covering the body. A silver-tipped bear with a dark stripe running down the back is called a "roachback." Rarely, silver tipping and light-colored fur creates a blond bear.

"Front-grizzled bears" are mostly medium to dark brown on the body with the face showing medium to heavy grizzling.

"Back-grizzled bears" show light to medium grizzling on the back but the front and rump are brown. On some bears the girth band behind the shoulders may be light-colored; this is the designation "saddleback."

"Dark bears" are dark brown to black with an occasional light-colored girth band.

All the color variations represent a mixture of genetic makeup, age, season, lighting, and environmental inputs. Paradoxical as it seems, the North American black bear can be black, brown, chocolate, reddish brown, cinnamon, blond, yellow, honey, red, bluish, or white. Black phases are most common in Yellowstone but brown phases are frequent. Restricted geographic locales characterize the blue or glacier bear of Alaska and the white black bear known as the Kermode

or spirit bear by British Columbia natives. Obviously it would be better to call all black bears by a different, colorless name (I prefer the name "American bear," *Ursus americanus*), but "black bear" is entrenched in common usage.

Muzzle color on black bears and grizzlies may provide distinctive individual appearances. Black bear muzzles are often a different color than their bodies. Some muzzles are strikingly brown or tan. A very light colored muzzle earns the bear the identifier, "baldface."

Young bears may change color during the first two years of life. Black bears may change from brown to black. Both black and grizzlies tend to lose the light-color neck yoke of youth.

Wear and molt (shedding) create dramatic color differences. While in the den, bears rub against dirt, rocks, or roots, wearing off their long winter hairs. Broken hairs reveal short new growth that shows strong coloration. An emerging bear can appear very two-toned if the pelage or fur is heavily rubbed. Following emergence, bears start to molt, giving the coat a ragged and blotchy appearance. Shedding is completed in July or August at which time new hair is short and sports a glistening sheen. As summer progresses the hair fades and becomes lighter due to sun bleaching. Grizzlies may be very dark with little silver tipping during late summer but as fur lengthens for winter, tipping becomes prominent.

Finally, lighting and weather can change the apparent color of a bear. In the shade, light girth bands may not show. In shade, light bears become dark. A wet bear always looks dark.

While describing color patterns is easy, explaining why different colors occur is not. Lynn Rogers, a friend and patriarch of black bear biologists, reviewed several ecological hypotheses about coloration. Black fur may be more resistant to abrasion. Therefore, black fur performs better in dense forests but is not needed in the open areas of the West. Alternatively, black individuals may be more susceptible to heat stress and do not do well in open meadows. Brown-phase black bears occur mostly where their potential predators, the wolf and grizzly, also occur. The brown pelage may serve as camouflage from predators or perhaps mimic the color of grizzly bears. But how do we explain the white and blue bears in dark rain forests of the Pacific Northwest? These theories are difficult to test, so we may never know.

Sensing their world

Vern Bailey, author of *Animal Life in Yellowstone* (1930), related an old Indian proverb, "If a pine needle fell, the eagle saw it, the deer heard it, and the bear smelled it." I often say a bear is "a nose on four legs."

Bears have an acute sense of smell. If the wind is blowing just right, grizzlies may pick up the odor of a carcass from several miles away. Bears may even navigate their territories by using "smell maps" in their brains.

On several occasions I have observed grizzlies searching for elk calves. A bear will travel back and forth through the sagebrush, sniffing the ground and air. Suddenly the nose rises to the winds and the grizzly changes direction and goes straight to a calf. The story is often told that elk calves lack an odor, but from handling afterbirths, fetuses during necropsies, and deceased newborns, I can tell you there is an odor and it stays on your hands. However, when the mother caches the newborn in the sagebrush, the odor may remain in a small area immediately around the newborn. To use a dog handler's term, the odor may "lay down." Additionally, wind across open areas may disperse any odor that rises above sagebrush level. Such conditions may make it more difficult for the bear to find a calf, but, nonetheless, bears are often successful because of their noses.

"In Lamar recently, my class and I watched as a sow grizzly chased an elk calf nearly a mile across the flats. Her COY could not keep up and was soon left behind. When the COY lost visual contact, the cub panicked and turned uphill, climbing out of the valley. After the mother had the calf down, she turned, looked, and panicked, not finding her cub. In a frenzy, she circled quickly and then hit her own odor trail. Nose to the ground she followed her trail back to the point she intersected the cub's trail. She made a right-angle turn onto the cub's trail and disappeared from our sight. Later she returned to her kill with her cub walking as fast as its little legs would take it." — FIELD NOTES

Bill Hamblin, Yellowstone roadside *ursophile* for the better part of two decades, related several days of bear watching in the fall of 2002. The Geode wolf pack was observed on an elk carcass. A grizzly came to the carcass and usurped it from the wolves. For two days the wolves and grizzly took turns feeding on the carcass until the meat supply was gone. The wolves left first. About 40 minutes after the wolves left, the grizzly turned, put its nose to the ground, and began to follow the wolf trail. For five days the grizzly followed either the Geode or Leopold packs by their scent trails.

We know wolves for their ability to smell, but perhaps the grizzly has a better nose. Nathan Varley, all-around ecologist, told of a time in Pelican Valley during late winter. Wildlife was scarce and wolves were hungry, not having made a kill for several days. A grizzly, fresh out of hibernation, entered the area and proceeded to dig through several feet of snow, finally pulling an old carcass to the surface where the bear, ravens, eagles, and wolves were able to scavenge.

The carcass was from earlier in the fall or winter. Why the grizzly and not the wolves chose to dig out the carcass is not clear. Nathan does not know if the wolves couldn't smell it, but obviously the bear did. Perhaps it was an energy/reward tradeoff. Digging may have been too energy costly for the wolves, but if the bear did it, then the carcass became worth scavenging.

George and Jana Stevenson, neurosurgeon, and neruroanatomist and biologist, are using MRI and CT technology to produce three-dimensional maps of Yellowstone grizzly brains. Their research reveals that the brains, while similar to other mammals, have an enlarged olfactory (smelling) apparatus. Compared to humans, a bear's olfactory region is about 250 times larger.

The bear's enhanced sense of smell is directly wired to the brain, a condition much more primitive than for other senses such as vision and hearing. This leads the Stevensons to believe that bears develop "smell maps" in their brains. Humans have "visual maps." A "smell map" allows a bear to navigate primarily by odors, augmented by vision and hearing.

The Stevensons also found larger somesethic (touch) and motor regions. The bears' enhanced sense of touch and motor skills probably allows bears to manipulate objects with their claws. I have observed grizzlies picking up single small pine nuts with their claws as if their claws were chopsticks.

An old hunter's tale is that bears do not see well. Perhaps this story is sparked by the bear's tendency to stand on its hind feet to

A subadult male grizzly stands on its hind legs to survey its surroundings. Bears often stand to see better over surrounding vegetation.

CUBS-OF-THE-YEAR

Mesmerizing! That's the only word to describe cubs-of-the-year (COY), the little, newborn bear cubs. Tourists, biologists, bear managers—all will watch the antics of COY for hours.

When born during the month of January, black bear cubs weigh less than 10 ounces. Grizzly cubs are a little heavier, weighing about a pound. Cubs are born hairless with their eyes sealed shut. Helpless, they rely on their mothers for warmth and nourishment.

Mothers nurse the cubs in the dens. Bear milk is more concentrated than that of most mammals and contains roughly 1 percent ash, 33 percent dry matter, and 18 percent lipids. Bear milk provides 2.3 Calories per gram, compared to about 9.3 Calories per gram for fat, 3.8 for carbohydrates and 3.1 for proteins. COY consume about 0.75 pounds of milk per day while in the den but as much as three pounds per day during the summer. Nursing mothers lose nearly twice as much weight per day as non-lactating females. For each pound lost by nursing mothers, a COY gains 0.7 pounds.

Nursing peaks in a cub's first summer but is greatly reduced by fall. I have observed grizzly cubs nursing during their second summer and on rare occasions trying to nurse during their third summer.

When COY exit their dens, they weigh about five to ten pounds. They gain about 40 to 50 pounds before denning again with their mothers in the fall.

In the spring, cubs-of-the-year are so small they can almost walk under their mother's stomachs. By fall they will have grown too big to even try.

BELOW LEFT: *A grizzly mother and two cubs-of-the-year.*

BELOW RIGHT *A black bear mother and cub-of-the-year.*

examine its surroundings. Rather than suggesting poor vision, I believe standing is an indicator of the bear's great ability to adapt. Even a big grizzly standing on all four legs is not much taller than the average sagebrush. By standing on its hind legs, the bear improves its view and increases its safety margin.

There are several components to vision including colors, shades, and the detection of outlines and movements. In the eye, cell structures known as rods detect light intensity and cones detect color. Compared to human eyes, bear eyes lack some types of cones so bears may not see all the colors that we do. Research suggests that bears may detect blue or green as something different than blue and green. They do see shades of gray from black to white.

Aside from potential differences in seeing colors, my experience suggests that bears see as well as humans. Bears are very good at detecting outlines and movements. Once I spent a considerable amount of time crawling up the side of a ridge to observe some elk. As I crested the ridge, to my surprise a grizzly stood bolt upright about a half mile to my left, looked at me and spooked off. I do not know whether it was my outline above the ridge or my movement that caught the bear's attention. I have seen hunting grizzlies patiently wait and watch as elk approached their hiding places.

Bears also hear well, as I can testify from the many times I have seen grazing bears look up at the sound of a human footstep. Bears know the difference between the footfalls of a quadruped versus those of a biped. They will startle at the sound of a human while seeming to ignore four-legged animals walking nearby.

However, there are situations when a hiker needs to remember that a bear's hearing may fail. Along a river a bear's hearing may be overpowered by the sound of rushing water. Wind may blow sound away. Dense vegetation may block sounds. These situations could lead to a startled bear and are best avoided.

2. THE BEAR YEAR

Each bear is an individual with its own personality. A docile, tolerant bear may "get up on the wrong side of the bed one morning" or, having been bullied by a larger bear, take out its aggression on the nearest object or animal. One bear may be lazy, another busy as a beaver. Individuality makes it difficult to study bears and to provide the generalizations that the public often wants.

For the scientist dealing with a subject, the first step is to summarize and describe average and baseline conditions. Next, scientists search for exceptions from the norm. Studying the deviations is the route to learning. To that end, I describe the Bear Year, *an average* of individual personalities modified by the forces of nature into an annual pattern. The Bear Year has five seasons: emergence, mating, summer, hyperphagia, and hibernation. Emergence, the season of renewal and beginning, begins when bears exit their dens in the spring and lasts until mid-May. Mating, the season of reproduction, runs from mid-May to mid-July. Summer, the season of growth, runs from mid-July to the end of August. Hyperphagia, the season of fattening, runs from the beginning of September to denning. Hibernation, the season of sleep and birth, runs from denning to emergence.

Emergence

Emergence from the den is a protracted affair for the individual bear and for the population as a whole. An individual bear may go in and out of its den for several days. For several days we watched a black bear near Elk Creek. She would exit her den each day and stay in front of it until she re-entered it to sleep each night. Then she made a bed outside of the den and slept there at night but during the day she also slept in the den. Finally she moved away from the den. Another black bear near the confluence of Soda Butte Creek and

A grizzly sits on the snow soon after emerging from hibernation in Yellowstone National Park. Bears may leave hibernation as early as late February; a few bears have usually been seen by mid-March.

Lamar River only poked her head out of her tree den for several days before she and her cubs came out.

Mark Haroldson of the IGBST reported that the first grizzlies to exit their dens are males, with some coming out as early as the last week of January. Nearly 30 percent of males are out of their dens before the first female comes out in the second week of March. Half the males are out by the third week of March. During the fourth week of March, females with cubs of the year begin to emerge. By the first week of May, 90 percent of all bears are out, but the last bears to emerge may be as late as the third week of May.

Following emergence, the physiological and biochemical state of hibernation decreases over a period of time that may last

two weeks. During this period of "walking hibernation," bears eat and drink little. Though active, urine output is low. They move down slope to winter ungulate range to commence feeding on winterkilled carcasses and greening vegetation.

Mating

The most complete record of breeding in grizzlies was provided by the Craighead brothers and it is their data I cite here. Although much of their research was at park garbage dumps, their information helps paint a better picture of the reproductive process.

The breeding season begins as early as May 14 when females enter a period known as estrus. The size of the vulva doubles, and females are receptive to advances by males. Estrus averages 11 days but may last as long as 27 days.

Correspondingly, male testes begin to enlarge before the bear leaves the den but sperm are not produced until late May. Testicular size is largest during the breeding season when the testes are descended. Their visual presence may aid in determining gender. By September testicular size has regressed and testes ascend into the abdomen before denning.

A female in estrus is readily identified by the number and behavior of males around her. Males test the female's receptivity by smelling her urogenital region. If the female is receptive, the male tries to isolate her from other males. He will trail her while they feed and seldom lets her out of his sight. Males often drive off other males. Pair bonds between males and females last from days to weeks.

Lactating females seldom mate, perhaps because lactation suppresses estrus. However, I have observed a female grizzly copulating while her two COY were nearby, and there is a report of a black bear emerging from her den with both yearlings and COY.

On a foggy day following a late spring snowstorm, one grizzly follows another. Perhaps it is a male checking out a potential mate.

On average, copulation lasts 24 minutes but can last for an hour. Conception may depend more on the length of the session than the number of sessions.

Females may be promiscuous, averaging about 5 copulations per breeding season and as many as 11 copulations in a season, sometimes with multiple males, even in one day. Lance Craighead, bear ecologist and geneticist, explained that his DNA analyses of northern grizzlies revealed that in as many as one-third of the litters the cubs in a litter had different fathers. Males will mate with as many females as possible. But not all matings result in cubs being born, especially if the female is a subadult.

The latest observed copulation was July 15, making the average breeding season 55 days. Most copulations occur in the first two weeks of June and 80 percent occur during that month. Mating activity is reduced by the end of the month.

Some females may reach puberty at three and a half years of age, the average age for producing a first litter is six years. Males may produce sperm by five years of age but because of dominance by bigger males, most males probably do not mate until six or more years of age.

Females often appear to have two periods of estrus during the breeding season. Between those periods, males may not show interest in the female until again tipped off by a pheromone odor.

Bears are thought to experience induced ovulation. In other words, females do not release eggs for fertilization until something during the mating behavior triggers the release. Biologists have suggested the trigger is the physical action of mating, but it may be something more general such as the presence or smell of a male.

The most intriguing part of the breeding process is delayed implantation. Once fertilized, the egg divides but then goes dormant. The egg floats within the womb without further development. If the female enters her winter den in a nutritionally weakened state, the eggs do not implant. Delayed implantation is an excellent means for a female in a harsh environment to avoid the physical drain of motherhood when she does not have adequate nutritional reserves. If the female has adequate weight and fat reserves, then the egg implants in late October or early November and development continues until birth, about 60 days after implantation.

Following mating, males and females dedicate their time and efforts to eating, growth, and for females with cubs, the protection of and rearing of cubs.

Summer

Summer is the time of growth. Bears reverse the weight losses of hibernation and finally regain their pre-hibernation weights. Energy no longer has to be spent on mating and is shifted to growth. Bears increase their sizes and weights, becoming larger and more powerful than they were the previous year. During the summer most of the increase in size appears to be in lean body mass (muscle). There is little addition of fat. However, towards the end of summer changes in body biochemistry and physiology begin to shift resources to fat accumulation.

During the late spring and summer, bears tend to move to higher elevations. They are following the "greening up" of forage plants as warming temperatures stimulate plant growth higher on the

In a summer meadow the natural curiosity of one grizzly cub leads it away from its mother and sibling. Perhaps it is a male; male cubs often stray farther than female cubs.

mountains. Bears also move to other food sources such as spawning trout and moth aggregation sites.

Hyperphagia

Hyperphagia is the intense biological drive to find and consume food that bears experience in the fall. Hyperphagia is the season of fat accumulation. The duration and rate of food intake increases dramatically. Bears will often go days without sleeping in order to eat. They gain significant weight, primarily fat. Weight gain may be as much as three pounds per day. A bear might gain 100 pounds during the month of September alone.

Roadside *ursophiles* notice behavioral changes that indicate hyperphagia. Bears may feed all day without sleeping or resting. Day after day, a bear may be in the same spot, often moving only a few hundred yards but constantly eating. Almost nothing distracts the feeding bear. The search for high energy, high quality foods is paramount, and this unrelenting drive often leads bears away from protected areas. Bears are drawn to food sources such as garbage, bird feeders, hunting areas, and hunting camps. Leaving the

During hyperphagia bears travel relentlessly in search of food. Here a grizzly bear prowls along Sedge Creek River in Yellowstone.

protection of remote reaches of the ecosystem often leads to negative encounters with people.

Hibernation

Hibernation is the season of "sleep." It can be broken into two phases: denning and the actual biological process of hibernation.

Denning

Denning is the physical act of selecting a site, preparing the den and nest, and entering the den for the final time to start hibernating. Environmental conditions trigger bears to start searching for dens and to ultimately crawl in for a long winter's sleep. Two factors are key: the availability of food and the arrival of winter weather. Cold and snow probably set the stage but the availability of food provides the final shove. Hungry bears hibernate; those with plenty of food don't. Some male Kodiak brown bears stay out all winter. They are finding enough food so that hibernation isn't necessary. Of course, zoos keep bears on display all winter by providing an ample food supply.

Interestingly, wolves may affect bear hibernation. With the natural return of wolves to Glacier National Park in northern Montana, carcasses provided by wolves (and cougars) may be providing enough food that some grizzlies are not hibernating. Since wolves were reintroduced into Yellowstone in the mid-1990s, bears appear to be remaining out longer in the fall and coming out earlier in the spring, but it is difficult to determine whether these changes are the consequences of greater food availability or mild winter weather of recent years.

A black bear den. Grizzlies dig about 90 percent of their dens while black bears dig only about 15 percent of their dens. Most dug dens collapse within a year.

ABOVE: *The author and one of his students explore an old cave in volcanic rock in Yellowstone. The cave is rumored to have served as a grizzly den, off and on, for hundreds of years.*

RIGHT: *Bears start moving into their dens as fall snowstorms arrive. Denning is an extended process that may span two months.*

There are few detailed studies of dens. John Mack provided much of our knowledge of black bear dens in the GYE while the Craigheads, Steve Judd, and other members of the IGBST provided the best information about grizzly dens. Grizzly and black bears show slight differences in denning locations. In general, grizzlies den on steeper slopes (33 degrees) than black bears (28 degrees). Grizzly dens are higher in elevation (7600 to 9200 feet, averaging 7990 feet) than black bear dens (5800 to 9150 feet, averaging 7390 feet). Both species tend to den on north slopes but all points of the compass are used.

Grizzlies, the digging bears, tend to prepare their dens by excavation (86 percent of the dens) but use natural cavities in caves (11 percent) and hollow white bark pine trees (3 percent). Black bears also dig dens but only about 43 percent of the time. Black bears also den in rock crevices, rock outcrops and talus, under boulders, and under stumps and roots. Often black bears are not too particular about their winter site and occasionally the den will be so shallow that the bear's rump is exposed. For at least two winters one black bear denned under the porch of Old Faithful Lodge. The hibernating bear could by seen by simply crawling under the porch.

Once the den is excavated or selected, some bears build nests in the den. Nests usually consist of spruce or fir boughs that the bear has chewed off and brought into the nest. Sometimes the nest may be 18 inches thick. Interestingly, some bears drag nesting material out of the den in the spring. The Craigheads reported that a female grizzly made her nest from moss and grass when she was pregnant but used tree boughs in the years when she wasn't pregnant. It is easy to speculate that she wanted a softer nest for newborn cubs. Both dens and nests may improve in quality as bears grow older and more experienced.

The Craigheads reported that grizzlies showed increasing lethargy before finally disappearing into their dens. While some bears den in September before any snowfall, other bears use their dens for temporary shelters during autumn snowstorms and then come out again. Finally, they simply do not come out again. Kerry Gunther,

bear biologist, has observed bear tracks in the snow leading into dens. Moving into a den during a snowstorm could cover the bear's tracks, thus conferring protection by reducing the ability of other animals to follow a bear to its den. Or it may simply be more comfortable to be inside a den during a snowstorm. Mark Haroldson reported that the first bears to enter dens are pregnant females, some of which enter dens as early as the third week of September. About half of the non-pregnant females have entered their dens by the first week of November, and about half of the males have entered by the second week of November. Ninety to ninety-five percent of all bears have denned by the first week of December. Undenned males have been observed in the last week of December.

The duration of denning varies with gender and the presence of cubs. Haroldson and colleagues with the IGBST determined denning durations for grizzlies as follows: males 131 days; females 151 days; and females with cubs 171 days. Males may spend as few as 125 days in the den while females with cubs may spend as many as 177 days.

Hibernation Biology

Hibernation and bears used to be fighting words, especially among earlier physiologists and small mammal biologists. They argued that since hibernating bears did not lower their body temperatures as low as hibernating rodents, bears were not true hibernators. However, based on nearly 40 years of intensive research by many scientists, bears should be deemed the most efficient hibernators of all, having the most highly evolved physiological and biochemical mechanisms for surviving periods of little or no food. So hibernation is the correct word for a bear's dormancy or torpor period of "winter sleep."

During hibernation, bears might not feed, urinate, or defecate for up to seven months. Body temperatures drop from normal levels of 98 to 101 degrees Fahrenheit to 88 to 95 degrees; heart rates drop from 40 to 50 beats per minute to 8 to 12 beats per minute; and a bear's basal metabolic rate drops to about 70 percent of its summer rate. Proportionately, the change in a bear's metabolic rate appears to be as great as that of a hibernating ground squirrel, and the bear's hibernation is probably more efficient than the squirrel's hibernation. And of course, during a pregnant bear's hibernation, cubs are born and nursed.

Roy Ozanne, my winter ecologist friend, and I explain the hibernation process in detail in our book, *Winter: An Ecological Handbook*. Here I paraphrase portions of that explanation.

One of the keys to this period of fasting is that bears are able to burn mostly fat instead of protein. Small rodents, on the other hand, must burn 10 percent of their protein supplies. In bears, glycerol from fat is turned into glycogen which can be used by the brain. The small amount of protein that gets metabolized leaves some nitrogen wastes in the form of urine. When proteins are metabolized, ammonia and bicarbonate are released. Both are poisonous but normally both are combined by the liver into a substance called urea which is excreted as urine.

The formation of urea during hibernation would be a problem because it requires water and the loss of water would cause dehydration. Instead, bears recycle urea to prevent toxic build up. During hibernation, urea is produced in the liver but released into the blood and excreted in saliva, which bears swallow. In the intestines, bacteria convert urea back to bicarbonate and ammonia. Other bacteria convert the ammonia into protein, completing the nitrogen recycling process.

The bacteria also produce acids which combine with bicarbonate to produce carbon dioxide and water. Water is, of course, reabsorbed and the carbon dioxide accumulates in the blood or may be passed from the body as flatulence.

A bear goes through hibernation using mostly fat for fuel and exits hibernation with about the same amount of lean body mass—muscle—as it had when it went into hibernation. It ingested neither food nor water. It excreted neither urine nor feces. It exchanged with its environment only oxygen, carbon dioxide, water, and heat. The whole process is very efficient. Bears are the best hibernators.

3. BEHAVIOR

A certain magic exists about bears. Something grabs the human imagination and "holds it hard like a spell," to borrow a phrase from Robert Service. Explaining that magic is difficult if not impossible. Perhaps some of the magic comes from bears appearing cuddly. Perhaps it is because bears sometimes walk upright like humans. Perhaps it is their size and ferociousness. How can something so big be so cuddly yet kill in an instant? I think much of the magic comes from bear behavior as a reflection of what we see in ourselves.

Curiosity

To me, the most endearing bear behavior is curiosity. Here are some examples.

Curiosity trumps fear

One evening along the road to the east gate we watched a male grizzly grazing nearby. It had been grazing for an hour when a speeding car skidded to a stop and the driver started honking the horn. With an explosive start, the bear bolted into the woods. We lingered, grousing (nice word) about our vehicular visitor as darkness arrived. We were about to leave when a bear nose appeared behind a nearby spruce. Cautiously, the same bear that had run away inched directly to the skid marks left by the car. It sniffed them and then, curiosity satisfied, returned to grazing.

Curiosity gets bears in trouble

One June a young grizzly discovered tents. Two of my students who had recently arrived from New York were camped in Indian Creek Campground. One morning they woke up as the wall of their tent visibly and noticeably flexed. The wall came in and then snapped

Bears are curious and playful. To this subadult grizzly bear, an old bone may be both nourishment and a toy.

out. It came in again and snapped out. And again. A grizzly was pushing on the tent with its paw. The bear would push on the side of the tent and then quickly jerk back its paw so the taut wall of the tent rebounded. The New Yorkers could see the grizzly through the thin tent fabric and were sure their lives were over. Before leaving New York their friends had told them a bear in Yellowstone would eat them. But with its curiosity satisfied, the young bear moved on. Ten campsites away, it sat on a tent with a husband and wife inside. The bear, a male, became known as "Tent Crusher." Needless to say the National Park Service couldn't tolerate that wayward behavior and trapped the bear for removal. And yes, the bait for the trap was a tent, set up in a nearby field.

Observant curiosity

Bear biologist Kerry Gunther related an instance of evidently premeditated curiosity. The two yearlings of grizzly 79 had created a traffic jam on Swan Lake Flats. Finally the yearlings left in the direction of Terrace Mountain, crossing a hiking trail. Kerry watched awhile and, after deeming it safe, walked to the trailhead sign. There he stapled a warning sign that read, "Bear Frequenting Area." Kerry walked back to the road, turned and looked back. The yearlings came out of the woods, walked directly to the new sign, grabbed it in their teeth and pulled it down. Evidently they had been watching Gunther from just inside the forest and were curious about what he had done.

Curiosity may allay fear

Susan Chin, a park biologist, was watching a grizzly in Pelican Valley when a spotter plane flew over. Susan figured the low flying plane would spook the bear and end her observation. But the bear heard the plane, looked up, and then stood up for a better look. According to Chin, the bear seemed be thinking, "What's that? Oh, it's not going to hurt me." Apparently satisfied, the bear dropped to all four feet and continued grazing.

Thinking and learning

Having observed thousands of bears across North America, I am impressed with their minds. No matter what some people say, it appears to me that bears think and learn. I am certainly not arguing that their level of thinking is comparable to humans, but processes of reasoning do seem evident.

Historical examples seem to show learning related to food. Bear biologist Dave Mattson noted how in a short period of time in 1986 bears learned to feed on a nutritional member of the parsley family, sweet-cicely, and how bears learned to find and feed on moths. A similar process may have occurred after the garbage dumps closed when bears began taking greater advantage of spawning trout.

Reasoning seems evident on a bear-by-bear basis. In 1980, as part of a bear class with Steve Mealy, we trapped grizzlies with Larry Roop of the Wyoming Game and Fish Department. Just northeast of the park Larry set a culvert trap. He obtained half of a cow for bait and one hindquarter was placed in the trap.

Having nowhere to store the remaining hindquarter, we hung it with rope from a tree branch near the trap. The branch was 20 feet above the ground, and it was the lowest branch on the tree. The tree was two feet in diameter and sloped at a 75-degree angle.

When we arrived the next morning, we were startled to see a grizzly lying on the branch. Tracks showed that the bear had stood on its hind legs below the meat but couldn't reach it. In an apparent attempt to reach the hindquarter, the bear had climbed the tree and onto the branch. Given time, might the bear have been able to grasp the rope and pull up the meat? I don't know but it seemed like the bear used reasoning to decide to go up the tree.

Late one day Kerry Gunther received a call about a dead black bear on a park road; the bear had been struck by a car. Kerry managed to slide the carcass up a piece of plywood and into the bed of his pickup. He drove to the park's freezer and put the carcass in it for later examination. Returning home about midnight, Kerry pulled the bloody plywood out of his truck and washed off the plywood and his truck with a garden hose. He dragged away the plywood and left it in his yard. Finally he collapsed into bed.

Kerry's cabin was inside the park on the plains just north of Sepulcher Mountain. The next morning Kerry looked out a window and saw a grizzly coming through the sagebrush. It walked straight to the truck, stood up, and looked into the bed.

Next the bear followed the scent trail across the yard to the plywood. The bear circled the plywood, looking curiously. It went to one end and lifted the board with a paw and looked underneath. Then the bear went to the other end and lifted the board to peer underneath. Then the grizzly walked away.

Kerry said it was as if the grizzly could smell the black bear but couldn't find it. The bear seemed to "think" the black bear was underneath the board and lifted the board to check. Finding nothing there, the bear moved on.

One fall day I was hiking alone on McMinn Bench. I was hiking across the flats but somewhat close to the western edge. Off to the east I spotted a large blond-colored black bear and stopped to watch.

The bear was "mousing" in three inches of fresh snow. After an unsuccessful effort, the bear looked around and spotted me. Without hesitation it started to amble over. I slowly backed towards the cliff behind me. The bear kept coming and narrowed the distance between us to maybe 50 yards. I looked over the cliff. It was eight to ten feet to a landing area on a steep slope. I thought I could drop down the cliff and leave the bear behind, but it would be dicey.

Do bears think? There is little doubt in the author's mind that bears do think and they certainly do learn. This young grizzly bear intently studies its surroundings.

The bear noted that I was looking at it and slowed down. Then it stopped and stared at me. I looked straight at it, not as a challenge but to let it know I was watching. Sensing I would not back down, the bear turned and walked away at a normal pace. It disappeared behind a small knoll.

I figured my best strategy was to stay still for a while. After five minutes, my patience gave out and I was about to move when a nearby motion to my left caught my eye. There was the bear. It had just appeared from behind a knoll it had apparently used to hide its approach. Closer now, the bear started to walk so it would pass right by me.

The bear walked near me but not directly at me. Its closest point was about 25 feet away. I considered making a ruckus, but I could see the bear was just curious, not aggressive. The bear turned its head and looked at me as it passed. Once past, it sped up to an amble and left.

I was amazed the bear had deliberately hidden its efforts to sneak up on me. It knew I was watching. By coming up behind the knoll it had cut the distance between us in half without exposing itself. Thinking? Reasoning? This is only one of many stories about the cunning of a bear.

Mothering behavior

The love of a mother bear for her cubs is legendary. It ranges from incredible tolerance and patience to tough love to unabashed defense. I have sat and watched for hours as mother bears wrestled with their cubs. Cubs climb all over mom, biting her ears, her lips, but neither a whimper from mom nor retribution.

A cub's teeth are sharp and they have to learn how hard to bite yet not cause injury when playing. Sometimes the bite is too hard and mom does yelp. Generally, the yelp is followed by a cuff with her paw. The cuff is a wondrous muscular action. Think for a moment about the mother bear's paw. It is large and armed with five powerful claws that can rip open a log or an animal. But when mom uses the paw on the cub, it is flat handed; the claws are not turned in. The force is attenuated to just the correct amount to teach the intended lesson.

During 2004 and 2005, roadside bear interpreter Mark Hanna worked on the Bear Safety through Education Program directing traffic at "bear jams." Most of Mark's time was spent around the Roosevelt-Tower area and Mark was able to observe many hours of mother and cub interaction. He kept notes about the collective responses of bears to people.

Mark recognized different styles of motherhood as exemplified by three examples of black bears. One female known by her red ear tag was very laid back, too casual to become alarmed at people or cars. A second female with two brown cubs was not as comfortable with people. She was very careful when she and her cubs had to cross the road. Twice she bluff charged people to get more room before crossing. One time two people were watching from the top of

This playful wrestling between a black bear mother and her cub may be more than play. It may be teaching the cub about serious fights that it will face later in life.

their van. The bear charged them as if to say, "Stay there." When startled, her reaction was explosive. She quickly sent her cubs up trees and ran in circles around the tree trunks. A third female with one cub liked to play more. She punched tents at Tower Campground.

Mark noted that each summer there was a general progression of female caution as if mother bears had a timetable for their cubs' development. In phase one, moms keep their cubs at a distance from the road. They may send their cubs up trees where the cubs stay for extended periods of time.

In phase two, the cubs are brought closer to the road. Cubs duplicate their mother in everything she does and quite literally stay next to her side. Usually they don't cross the road very much during this phase. At the slightest car noise or people disturbance, the whole family runs away from the road.

In phase three, the cubs still follow their moms but she lets them move further away from her. Families cross the road regularly. When there is a disturbance, the cubs scurry up a tree on their own. Mom doesn't have to tell them. The cubs don't stay in trees for as long as they used to stay.

Curious, fearless, or fearful, black bear cubs-of-the-year seek safety, refuge, solitude, and air conditioning in the tree tops. Black bear cubs are nimble tree climbers, ascending rapidly when frightened and when ordered to climb by their mothers.

In phase four, cubs go to the road on their own and mom follows. Cubs cruise the road out of curiosity and mom often has to signal the cubs to climb trees.

In the final phase, cubs check out people and venture far from mom. When startled they still run to mom's side but now it takes a "big" scare to make them climb trees.

I am amazed at the level of tolerance for people developed by some mother bears. Once I watched a black bear near Roosevelt sit on the ground and nestle two nursing cubs to her chest. Within ten feet of her, forming a complete circle, were people taking photos and admiring the "wild scene." Anthropomorphic as it might seem, the mother bear just seemed to say, "Oh, well."

Though a mother bear's tolerance for exploratory freedom by her cubs advances across the course of summer, she is still a disciplinarian. Let a cub make one slip of protocol and it immediately feels her tough love. A cub wandering too far away will be picked up by the nap of the neck or even an ear and brought back screaming to where it should be. Let the cub play too hard with a sibling or mom

and mom's cuff will send it rolling head-over-heels. A trip too far away from mom may also bring a cuffing.

Crossing a stream may be analogous to crossing a road. There is a first time and mastering the process may require tough love. I have watched as mother bears crossed streams and their cubs would go to the water's edge but not step in the water, no matter how much mom coaxed.

Judy and Gary Norris, long-term *ursophiles*, reported a grizzly with two COY near Soda Butte. After crossing the road with her cubs, mom approached two streams. At the first stream the cubs balked when she crossed. She gave a low "woofing" sound and the cubs jumped in and swam across. Out on the flats the grizzly stood and looked around for something that was bothering her, perhaps an odor or a sound. They then turned to the second stream, only this time the crossing was much deeper. One COY was caught in the current and washed downstream. Mom stood in the middle of the flats, apparently not paying attention to the cub. A hundred yards downstream the cub finally gained the shore and raced back to mom.

The toughest of tough love comes when it is time for a mother to send her young on their own way. For black bear cubs, this often happens at a year and a half; for grizzlies it usually happens at two and a half years. Mothers may trick cubs by sending them up a tree and then leaving, or they may get physically aggressive towards a cub, cuffing it until it gets the message.

One way or another, the cub finds itself alone. Judy Norris noticed that young bears in their first year after their mothers rejected them seemed particularly lost, lonely, and curious. One spring there was a

A young black bear pauses to groom its coat. When first separated from its mother, a young bear may be traumatized and mope around for days on end. Newly separated youngsters may even lose weight.

Mother bears often locate and identify their cubs by smell. If a cub strays away, the mother bear follows the cub's scent trail great distances to find it.

young runt of a black bear whose mother had kicked it out by treating it roughly and running it off. Nevertheless, the cub tried to stay as close to her as it could. For a long time the cub hung around where it could see her, hear her, or smell her.

On the other hand, there is nothing as desperate as a mother bear that loses her cubs. Nathan Varley told me about the time he was alone on a ridge near Jardine, just north of the park. Sitting and taking a break, Nathan thought about the female black bear and her three COY that he had seen 30 minutes earlier, feeding on berries. Suddenly the mother bear and the cubs popped onto the ridge three feet away from him!

Nathan kept still, perhaps too still.

The mother bear took a step towards Nathan, trying to figure out what he was. Nathan moved and she bolted. The cubs could not see where mom went and were left standing there. Only five feet from Nathan, the curious cubs stood and looked at him.

Worried that he had accidentally separated mom from her cubs and knowing he might not be in a safe situation, Nathan rolled over and crawled into the trees not far away. He could hear the cubs bawling, calling for mother. Four to five minutes later the mother bear came back. Nathan watched the rendezvous. She quickly took her cubs and ran off, intent on putting distance between her family and the human.

If cubs are lost, mothers have a special way of finding them: they track them by smell. On three occasions I have watched female grizzlies lose their COY during elk chases. After making the kill and in varying states of extreme agitation over their lost cubs, the females turned back on their own trails. Putting their noses to the ground, all three quickly ran back until their noses told them where the cubs' trails diverged. The mothers followed the cubs' scent trails out of sight and in all cases soon returned with the cubs in tow. The moms rapidly returned to their kills and it was all the cubs' short legs could do to keep up.

The scariest grizzly situation I ever witnessed involved a mother bear defending her cubs. It was 1980 and we were live-trapping grizzlies with Wyoming biologist Larry Roop. A culvert trap had been set in the middle of a large open meadow.

A culvert trap is made from a ten-foot section of heavy metal pipe, the same type of pipe placed under roads for drainage. About three feet in diameter, one end is welded shut and the other is fitted with a vertically sliding trap door. Bait is placed inside the open trap, and when a bear climbs in and pulls on the bait, a trigger mechanism connected to the bait releases the door and it slides down, trapping the bear inside. Basically the bear traps itself; no human has to be present. A culvert traps usually sits on a small trailer that can be towed into place and towed away with a bear in it. A culvert trap weighs several hundred pounds. Since bears are active at night, traps are usually checked the first thing every morning.

At daylight our group made its way along a trail to the meadow. While deep in the forest and separated from the trap by a low ridge, we heard the loudest commotion you can possibly image in a natural setting. To us the sound was unintelligible; it was like a cacophony of hell breaking loose. There were rapid metallic thuds and rumbles intertwined with hoarse growls, all repeated several times in quick succession, and then silence. A few minutes later the noise would start up again.

Intimidated, we decided it was better to see what was going on from some distance away rather than approach the trap on the trail, so we sneaked through the forest to a ridge with a view. We crawled up the ridge and saw the culvert trap a couple of hundred yards away. All we saw was the trap.

Then it all happened fast. An adult grizzly came rushing into view from behind the trap. It was foaming at the mouth and circling the trap in a frenzied state. Dust from its rapid circling hung in the air. All was deathly quiet for a moment, and we still didn't understand. Then from inside the trap came the bawling of a cub. Mother bear spun on her heels and attacked the trap. With one mighty swat of a paw she lifted the heavy trap a foot off the ground. The trap landed with a ferocious reverberating thud and from inside the trap came a barrage of bawling. Mom would slap the trap again and again. Finally mom would stop hitting the trap and all the noise would die down. A few moments later a cub would bawl and the whole high-intensity sequence started anew.

Biologists will tell you there are no records of a grizzly bear attacking a group of five or more people. But that morning our group of 20 people was not at all confident in that fact. To this day I believe that mother bear would have taken on all of us. Feeling chastised, we slunk off the ridge to the trail.

Back at the road a daring plan was hatched. A helicopter was flown over the trap, scaring away the mother bear. Then the helicopter hovered over the trap while a biologist, dangling from the helicopter on a rope, grabbed the trap door and raised it. Not one but two cubs scampered out, and then we understood the whole story. Isolated inside the trap, the cubs would soon get to fighting. One would hurt the other and it would bawl.

Mom, hearing the bawling, would run forward and swat the trap, scaring the cubs and making them bawl even more. Mom would swat again. Only when mom got tired of swatting did the bawling die down. But soon the cubs would start it all over again. After the cubs were released the family reunited and ran off.

Hikers, campers, and others who travel in bear country are told there are three things you don't do with a bear: surprise it, get near its food, and get between a mother and her cubs.

Just outside the east gate of Yellowstone is the cafe/motel called Pahaska Tepee. It often serves as meeting center for *ursophiles*. One spring we had been watching a female grizzly with a reputation for charging anyone who got too close to her young. Who decided when a person got too close? The grizzly did.

One morning our looking for the bear and her COY had been futile, so we retreated to a cup of coffee in the cafe. A tourist came in and announced he had just seen a grizzly and cubs come to the roadside by the bridge less than a half mile away. We bolted for the door.

Once outside we could see the bridge, and there was the grizzly with her cubs. So was a tragedy in the making. Approaching the cubs were two children, each perhaps five years old. Above them on

the shoulder of the road were their parents, cameras in hand. As we watched, the parents gestured for the children to get closer to the bears for a picture. Panic stricken, we dashed to our vehicles and sped to the bridge. When we arrived, the children were only about 25 feet from the cubs. The mother bear was watching them. We jumped out of the cars. Two of us held bear spray. No one breathed. No one spoke for fear of startling the mother bear.

The human parents snapped their picture and their kids clambered back to the road. Needless to say, when the kids were safe the parents were told of their dangerous and foolish actions.

A mother grizzly provided for her cubs by securing an early spring bison carcass. After feeding, bears may cover a carcass with dirt and vegetation to hide it from other carnivores and scavengers. Later they will return to feed again.

There is no doubt in my mind that nothing happened because somehow the mother bear knew the approaching humans were children, and that children were not a threat. I believe children are recognized by all mammals. There is also no doubt in my mind that had either parent approached the cubs, the outcome would have been drastically different.

Play

As children will be children, cubs will be cubs. Cubs are curious and playful. One spring we encountered a grizzly with a cub of the year. Mom was not 100 percent comfortable with people and started to walk away, but, as with children, when cubs don't want to move their little legs, not much progress is made. Every fifteen feet the little one would stop, turn towards us, and stand on its hind legs to look at us. Sensing mom moving away, it would drop to all four feet and scamper about fifteen feet towards her before curiosity got the best of it again. Then it stopped and sneaked another look at us. This went on for 150 feet, to mom's consternation. Finally they disappeared into the forest.

Judy Folts, Yellowstone's deputy chief of interpretation, told stories about "Tent Crusher." When he and his siblings were not bouncing on tents, they used Mother Nature as a playground. Judy watched them on a hillside south of Indian Creek Campground. The cubs would run up the hill and then roll back down, end-over-end. Back up the hill they would go and roll down again. The cubs seemed to "like" their playground.

We all know cubs love to wrestle and will do so for hours. Occasionally adults will play for a long time, too.

No Toys-R-Us exists for bears, so finding a toy is a red-letter event, even for an adult. Much of the time a stick serves as a toy. Bears will sit and play with a stick, juggling it between their paws, nipping on its end.

One time Kerry Gunther found a large orange playground ball when he was kayaking on the Yellowstone River outside of the park. Kerry took it back to his cabin and threw it in his yard. Later Kerry watched as a grizzly came into his yard and went right to the ball. The bear rolled on its back and picked up the ball with all four feet and began a balancing act. The bear left only when the ball was thoroughly shredded by its claws. I wonder if this was the same bear that came into the yard searching for the black bear under the plywood. Maybe it keeps an eye on Kerry's activities just to see what fun it can have.

Few people know that bears will play with other species. Wayne and Mary Ann Kendal, ardent *ursophiles* and *lupophiles* too, once spent nine hours watching and videotaping a wolf playing with grizzly cubs. When first spotted, the grizzly and her two COY were headed

During the day all the animals took short naps within 25 or 30 yards of each other. Between naps they played. Late in the afternoon the wolf approached the mother bear within five or six feet. Suddenly she jumped up and appeared to swat at the wolf. The wolf ambled off, occasionally looking back. Play day was over.

Sleep

No compilation of behavioral stories would be complete without the most common bear behavior of all. Visitors, photographers, and *ursophiles* line the park roads hoping for hot bear action, a glimpse of a cute cub, the photo of a lifetime, but Judy Norris' story sums it up. Along the road north of Norris Geyser Basin, a fine, dark grizzly traversed the hillside. It shuffled through snow, stepped over debris, and walked on a fallen log as well as any gymnast. Judy's hopes for seeing interesting behavior rose as the bear came closer. Then it

into a grove of aspen. The Kendals saw another black animal and thought it might be a third cub, but closer observation revealed it to be a yearling wolf (number 53M). The wolf approached the bears and neither cubs nor wolf seemed afraid.

Interactions began. The wolf approached as if he were going to grab a cub but never did. He would sniff the cub and then run away, skittishly, and the cubs would chase him. The mother bear allowed the back and forth play for a long time but seemed to limit how far away she would let the cubs go. When the cubs would get 30 feet from her, she would rush ahead and stand sideways in front of them, stopping them from going further. When the female would lie down, the wolf would creep in again.

When the grizzly began to nurse her cubs, the wolf laid down 10 yards away. He put his head on his paws and watched. The impression was that he would have nursed too.

Roadside watchers wondered if the wolf was trying to grab a cub because wolves are known to kill bear cubs. Wayne and Mary Ann believed the wolf had opportunities to grab a cub but never did. The wolf's behavior appeared curious and playful rather than aggressive.

A grizzly yawns before taking a mid-day nap. Sleeping bears are fairly common sights to bear watchers

burrowed under a tangle of deadfall on the snowy slope and fell asleep. Even as an avid bear-watcher, I do get tired of viewing the backsides of sleeping bears. For photographers and watchers, it is the "laughing backside" syndrome.

Fear

Bears are big, fierce, savage, and fearless. Wrong! As Klari Lea, bear aficionado from Vince Shutte Bear Preserve, says, "Bear are *fearful*, not *fearless*." A bear's life is one of danger, and three things in particular scare them: other bears, the unknown, and people.

Bears are wary of other bears until they have ascertained the other bear's size and temperament. One spring at Junction Butte pond there was a carcass in the forest about 50 feet from the road. For several days a small black bear would come off the hill at daylight and feed. After awhile a medium-sized black bear would come down, and the first bear would reluctantly leave. After some more time, a third, bigger black bear would arrive, and the second bear would move away.

One morning "Small" had been moved off by "Medium." "Big" came down and merely by its presence shoved a very disgruntled

Medium off the carcass. With knees locked, Medium stomped off about 50 feet, smashing every bush along the way. Medium then attacked a lodgepole pine, buffeting it with a left paw and then the right. Eventually Medium sat down and picked up a deer antler in its paws. The bear vigorously chewed on the thick end of the antler, obviously letting out aggressive feelings. Later I picked up the antler; its end was shredded into slivers the size of toothpicks. In this case, fear of a larger bear led to displacement behavior. Afraid to take out its aggression on the bigger bear, Medium displaced its behavior by beating up bushes and antlers.

The unknown is a powerful source of fear. Once I observed a large grizzly fishing on a stream. Earlier in the day the grizzly had won its spot by showing dominance over another bear, making that bear give way. All of a sudden a small, rambunctious black bear charged noisily down the hill and splashed into the center of the stream. Without pausing to check the source of the sudden noise and commotion, the frightened grizzly simply exploded out of the stream, up through the forest and out of sight.

Mother Nature can throw unknowns at bears. A student of mine, Veryl Goodnight, explained an experience we shared and videoed. High on Mount Washburn we watched a very blond adult grizzly grazing a half mile away. An approaching thunderstorm darkened the sky, dramatically emphasizing the vastness of the wilderness around us.

Rain came first, followed by hail. Our grizzly grazed on. Then came the first clap of thunder. It was distant but the lightning had

---

Bears are fearful, not fearless. Any sudden or strange sight, sound, or smell immediately puts a bear on alert, into a fearful posture, or starts it fleeing. For this black bear, a nearby noise could mean an approaching grizzly bear or some other danger.

illuminated our surroundings under the dark sky. We retreated to the bus where I kept videoing. Rain and hail slanted down. As the storm neared, the thunder grew louder. Now with each thunderclap the grizzly visibly jumped.

Suddenly a bolt of lightning exploded close to us. My video flashed overexposed and thunder rocked the sound track. The flash was instantly followed by a quick, sharp thunderclap, and the grizzly ran a short distance. Then came a huge, deafening burst of thunder. The grizzly reared up on its hind legs and danced around, looking right, then left, to see where the danger was. There came another close, loud thunderclap and the bear stood up again, visibly frightened. The pose was not like that of the taxidermist showing a bear about to attack. The pose showed fear. The bear was scared and was trying to find the source of the danger. Finally the bear dropped to all fours and galloped into the forest.

The bear's fear was the same fear that some dogs show in a thunderstorm. We came to the wilderness thinking the grizzly was the most ferocious animal in North America, but this bear was scared, even though storms in the high mountains are part of its life. It was another revelation about bears.

To a bear, surprise is a great unknown. One day I was rapidly hiking through the forest and leaped onto a large boulder. To my surprise— and the bear's, too—a black bear was laying in a day bed on the other side of the boulder. I remember seeing daylight below the bear's feet as it jumped into the air, vaulting about 30 feet away. Then it looked at me. It looked at a pine tree. It stood, reached up, and grasped both sides of the tree with its front legs. Glaring at me, the bear dug its claws into the tree trunk and slashed them down the tree. Ten vivid claws marks served as a message. Displacement behavior? Warning? I chose not to find out and respectfully backed away.

One way fearfulness promotes survival is through the ability to fight, to appease, or to flee a more dominant bear. For a bear like this grizzly to live to old age, conflict avoidance is the best strategy.

Fear, respect, or conflict avoidance, it is all part of a bear's nature for dealing with humans. One fall day on national forest land adjacent to Yellowstone, Judy Norris was eating lunch on a hillside and watching a large, cinnamon-colored black bear munching on something in the middle of a meadow. Near the meadow was a hiking trail. A couple of hikers with a dog came along. Sensing their approach, the bear drifted into the woods. Hikers and dog passed through the meadow where the bear had been and even the dog showed no signs of knowing the bear had been there. Once they were gone, the bear came back out.

One fog-shrouded morning south of Hayden Valley, several of us parked in a pullout in the forest next to the Yellowstone River. We came to view a carcass in the river. I exited the car first and the others followed. We were 75 feet from the cars when I looked back.

A bear nose poked out between our cars. Then two noses appeared. Four eyes cautiously looked around a fender at the people. My friends were following me and I held up my fingers to silently signal them. They spun around to see a pair of two-year-old grizzlies between our cars. The bears had climbed out of the river after feeding on the carcass and were trying to sneak across the road into the forest. When they realized they had been seen, they broke from the cars and sprinted into the trees.

Personal space

Fear relates to a sense of "personal" space. We know when others step into "our" personal space and so do bears. Personal space is the area within which a bear feels comfortable and not threatened. That space may vary on a day-to-day basis and is certainly different between individual bears.

Bears know the rules of personal space when encountering other bears. Subtle body language and vocal signals tell other bears when

they are infringing and when to stop. These rules and signals prevent most encounters from becoming physical confrontations.

Space requirements are different for different groups of bears. Coastal brown bears often gather in large numbers where food is abundant and relatively long lasting, such as whale carcasses or salmon streams. As a result, these bears are more social, their personal spaces smaller, and they tolerate other bears and humans quite close.

Grizzlies, on the other hand, are solitary bears that seldom have access to large sources of food. When food is found, there is usually a limited amount, such as a single carcass. As a result, grizzlies are far more likely to aggressively defend a food supply. A grizzly's personal space is large, and neither others bears nor humans can get close without invoking its ire.

Bears may become stressed long before space infringement causes them to make an overt reaction, either flight or fight. Their heartbeats may speed up and hormones may be secreted. These sorts of reactions cost energy, and bears prefer to conserve energy. Bear expert Steven Herrero suggests we consider a new term for a bear's personal space. He and his colleagues call it the "overt reaction distance (ORD)." ORD recognizes that when a bear reacts from an intrusion into its personal space, energy has already been spent. In fact, energy may be spent without any visible reaction. Therefore, the courteous bear watcher should stop his/her approach before entering the ORD. It's safer and healthier—for the bears and the bear watchers.

FACING PAGE: *Each bear, including these two grizzlies, is an individual with its own personal space. Intrusion into that personal space results in body signals warning the intruder to stop or to leave. Humans should recognize and respond to these signals.*

RIGHT: *Along Yellowstone's roads, adaptable bears habituate to the proximity of people in exchange for access to natural foods. Careful management of people allows bears such as this black bear to utilize important roadside habitat.*

Habituation

Sometimes bears seem to lack a protective fear of humans. Often to the joy of hundreds of visitors, a bear will graze or do other bear things near the road. Fear is suppressed because the bear is familiar with human behavior in such situations. Through experience, the bear knows that people will stay on the road and stay at a certain distance. Let a person violate either assumption and the bear often moves off quickly. Familiarity breeds habituation, or tolerance of people.

Habituation is but one facet of perhaps the most remarkable behavior by bears: adaptability. Roadside bears adapt to being near people by adapting to "rules" that are acceptable to people and bears.

Roadside watchers grow complacent with docile, habituated bears because most haven't experienced another bear behavior: sudden, violent change. Few have ever witnessed a bear "go ballistic." I have, four times. Four times my underwear turned brown and I thanked the powers that be that I was not the object of the bear's aggression. I wish I could fully share these experiences but words fail to express how rapidly and violently bears can change their moods. I'll share one story, although it is not a Yellowstone story.

My class and I had been watching brown bears along the coast of Katmai National Park in Alaska. Early on our second day I took my class upstream where a stream emptied out of a narrow gorge. I nestled the class on a gravel bar in plain view so any approaching bear would see us. The 15-foot-wide river separated us from a grassy meadow backed by a high cliff.

Fifteen minutes after we arrived a large female with three COY approached on the far side of the river. Her gaze told me she approved of our low demeanor and respectful silence. She closed the distance between us to less than 100 feet. I knew that moving would spook her, so we remained still. Since she seemed to approve of our presence, we photographed and videoed respectfully, all the while thankful for her sharing time with us.

The bears fished. They grazed grass. For a while it was idyllic. Then a cub's head went up. Then three cub heads looked upstream. Mom looked upstream. We knew something was happening but didn't know what. Mom shooed the cubs into a small ravine where they started climbing.

At that moment a large male bear came into view upstream. I emphasize the word "large." My class thought the female was big, and she was by Yellowstone grizzly standards. But the male was almost one and a half times as big as the female.

Seconds are much too long to measure the female's transformation from docile mother to roaring dervish. Frothing at the mouth and with her fur flared up, the female reared on her hind legs and charged the male. The male stood on his hind legs and the female went for his throat. Dodging and batting, he fended her off while backing away. It was as if he were trying to say, "Lady, all I wanted to do was fish." Finally they both dropped to all fours. Using the tip of her nose, she swung it sideways against his head three times, clearly motioning for him to leave. He backed off and she turned towards her cubs.

The male started into the river towards us. Thinking he might be in a very bad mood, I warned my class to grab their packs. However, once in the river the male turned downstream, passed us, and caught a fish. He was also tolerant of our presence.

For those who watch along the roads, be careful. You are playing by the bear's rules, and bears decide when those rules change. Susan Chin witnessed a bear jam control action near Beaver Lake. The grizzly was female 264, a popular roadside bear who on that day was grazing into the Beaver Lake Picnic Area. Park ranger Keith Young arrived to do crowd control.

Keith was managing the people as 264 grazed within 20 yards of the crowd. Keith had managed to move people to the east side of the road, giving the west side to 264. Keith was standing on the road and talking to the crowd with his back to the bear. For no apparent reason, 264 abruptly stopped grazing and walked with purpose to a tree right beside Keith. He jumped back. The bear sniffed and dug for a moment. Then she went back to the borrow pit and resumed grazing.

No one could understand why she came to the tree or why she dug. However, the message is that bears know when people are not looking and may take advantage of an off-guard moment to change the rules.

Homing

Another, almost legendary behavior of bears is their homing ability. As soon as managers started trapping and moving bears, they learned that bears could quickly find their way home. One such event of his youth impressed Lance Craighead, executive director of the Craighead Environmental Research Institute.

About 1963 an orphaned grizzly cub appeared along the road in Hayden Valley. Lance doesn't remember if they even knew what happened to the cub's mother. The cub created major traffic jams so rangers trapped it and moved it deeper into Hayden Valley. The cub quickly returned and was trapped again, with the same result. Now it was constantly on the road and Lance and others feared for its life.

The cub was captured again. This time it was

taken by boat across Yellowstone Lake and released on the Promontory. One week later the cub was back in Hayden Valley. Even today Lance doesn't know how the cub found its way back. Maybe it involved a visual clue such as Mount Washburn. A bear's innate homing ability is powerful and obviously develops at a young age.

Breeding

John Craighead, Jay Sumner, and John Mitchell in their book, *The Grizzly Bears of Yellowstone: Their Ecology in the Yellowstone Ecosystem, 1959-1992*, provided the most detailed coverage of grizzly breeding in Yellowstone. Most of their research dealt with bears at garbage dumps and is not applicable to solitary, free-ranging bears. I am indebted to them for many details of the breeding process. My personal observations of grizzlies, mostly along Antelope Creek and Lamar River, combined with the thoughts of Pam (Gontz) Cahill, Steve and Marilyn French, and Jim Garry led to the development of the following account of breeding behavior.

Biologists define the mating period as May 15 to July 15. Breeding can be thought of as four steps: 1) courtship, 2) rejection, 3) acceptance, and 4) copulation.

Courtship starts when a male detects a female coming into estrus. The clues to estrus are olfactory, and a male sniffs the female's genital region for pheromones (sexual hormones). If the male detects signs of estrus, he may follow the female wherever she goes, day and night. They may be side by side or he may lag behind as much as 200 yards. The male's usual proximity is about 15 to 20 feet behind the female and following her like a puppy follows its master. (Whenever two grizzlies are sighted together during the breeding period, look for a difference in size. A large bear with a small bear suggests a courting pair.) Sometimes a courting pair may stay together more than a week. During courtship a male will aggressively fend off other males.

A period of rejection is often intertwined with courtship. An unreceptive female may thwart a male's advances by simply sitting down. She may also growl aggressively, bite or swat at the male, or simply wander off. Determined males keep following. Females seem choosy, driving off some males yet encouraging others with submissive behavior.

When the female starts estrus, she becomes receptive to the male and a period of acceptance follows. Usually acceptance begins with the male smelling the female's genitals. He might try to mount

During mating season, adult male bears like this large grizzly travel great distances searching for females. When a receptive female is located, the male may stay with her for weeks

her but the female slips out from underneath. At first the acceptance ritual may be very rough and tumble as he tries to mount her and she dislodges him. A fair amount of swatting may occur between the animals.

Sometimes the male almost seems to lack interest. If this happens, the female may nuzzle or playfully bite at the male's neck. Sometimes she may lay down on her back with her legs spread. She may walk away, looking back to signal the male to follow.

During copulation the female stands on all four legs and the male mounts over the back. He will grab her with his front legs just behind her front legs. To secure his position, as it is sometimes a wild ride, he will often bite her neck or shoulder. Copulation usually lasts more than 20 minutes.

From their observations, Craighead, Sumner, and Mitchell believed the female's first copulations each season were the most productive. If initial copulations result in fertilized eggs, subsequent copulations may not have the same result. This might explain why dominant males do not defend females later in their estrus periods.

4. BEAR SIGNS

During their comings and goings, bears leave signs such as tracks and scat that are visible to the watchful observer. Bear signs tell us about bears, their habits, and their behaviors. It is a bear-wise hiker who knows the signs of bears and is able to discern fresh sign from old sign.

Bear trees

We call it Bear Valley, our secret location in Yellowstone. Walking along its narrow bottom, you can feel the presence of grizzlies and black bears. Interestingly, we seldom observe a bear in the valley. But at the upper end of the valley sits an art gallery of bear claw marks etched in the white bark of aspens. Each tree etched by claws is a fragile and temporary record of ursine comings and goings, and as with Anasazi petroglyphs of the southwest, we strive to understand their meanings.

Dr. Charles Jonkel, a renowned bear biologist, introduced me to "bear art," a term possibly more appropriate than Chuck realized. Art, while a form of expression and communication, is also fragile and transient. So, too, is bear art. The recording media, the tree, is temporary and short-lived. Fires may further shorten the record. In Yellowstone, most of the aspens are mature and are not being replaced. Therefore, most bear art in the park will disappear during my lifetime.

Bear trees (**FAR LEFT**) *are the "art" of the ursid community. As art, bear trees are an expression of presence and communication. They are also fragile and temporary. Many claw marks are made by climbing bears, but bears also claw trees to communicate their presence to other bears or, such as this black bear* (**NEAR LEFT**), *to displace "anger" at being moved off a food source by a more aggressive bear.*

FACING PAGE: *A young black bear vigorously claws into a rotten tree trunk, spewing "sawdust" like a chainsaw. This action opens a hole where the bear may find various kinds of insects.*

Bear art made this special place a "throne room" for our colleague and ursid lover, the late Dr. Elaine Anderson. Elaine was most alive when she stood with her students where the bears ruled. It is here that P.J. Kremer, Jim Garry, and I remember her best and may her memories reside here until bears no longer walk the planet Earth.

Bears mark trees in three manners: clawing, biting, and rubbing. Claws, teeth, and hair leave distinctive patterns. Trees with soft bark, such as aspen, take impressions well. Marks on conifer trees are less conspicuous. Bears usually scratch trees while standing on their hind feet.

To understand the tree marks, the first order of business is to determine what species made them. In addition to bears, cats and mustelids (members of the weasel family, such as a wolverines) mark trees. Some generalities help differentiate species. Look carefully: are there four or five claw marks? Cats typically leave four claw marks, while mustelids usually leave five claw marks per print. Bears may leave five claw marks per print but often the little toe does not leave a mark.

Cats and weasels both have very sharp claws. Bear claws are blunt and 0.02 to 0.3 inches wide near the tips. The claw marks of cats and weasels leave a signature consisting of a wide-narrow-wide patterns: narrow (.02 inches) at the beginning before the claws completely dig in, wider in the middle of the mark, then narrow again just before exiting. In contrast, bear claw marks are normally wide from beginning to end.

Bears like to mark prominent trees and if the tree looks prominent to you, check it for claw marks. Trees that occur at trail junctions are particularly good targets. Some trees seem to be clawed by every bear that passes by. One tree at the southeast corner of Timbered Island in Grand Teton National Park has been freshly clawed every year of the 34 years I have visited it.

Besides trees, bears seem to take great pleasure in marking human structures. Telephone poles, wooden bridge railings, trail signs, and building corners are often marked by bears.

When bears climb trees, they leave two patterns of claw marks: ascending and descending. On ascent, hind claws create slightly curved arcs of five round holes as the bear kicks its short, straight claws straight into the bark. The longer, more curved front claws make longer slices in the bark at an angle about 40 degrees from vertical. Climbing bears stand on their hind claws but hang from their front claws.

On descent, nearly vertical, longer cuts are often created when the bear slides down the trunk. These slashes are usually made by front claws but can be made by hind claws.

Two basic gaits are often impressed on the bark during a simple climb. The most common pattern consists of parallel impressions of claw marks: both front feet at about the same height, and both hind feet at another height. The gait is somewhat reminiscent of an inchworm's locomotion. Both hind feet kick into the tree at the same time and at the same height while both front feet reach up and grab the tree at the same time, same height. Then the bear again pulls up its hind feet and kicks the claws into the tree, and the front feet reach higher. This is a *very* fast way of climbing.

The other pattern consists of alternating ascending claw marks (as in left foot, right foot, left foot, right foot). Each foot grabs the tree at a different height, as if the bear were "crawling" up the tree. During both gaits the front feet reach around to the side of the tree, allowing the bear to hang from its front claws.

Both species of Yellowstone bears climb trees. Black bears climb trees throughout their lifetimes. Grizzly cubs less than a year old

Even though adult grizzlies are not expert tree climbers, good food often provides the incentive to reach great height. This grizzly clambered up an apple tree on the outskirts of Yellowstone National Park. Grizzlies have also been observed high in whitebark pine trees. KERRY GUNTHER

climb trees, though less frequently than black bear cubs. With increasing age, grizzly claws grow longer and straighter and the bears grow heavier, and both factors reduce the grizzly's ability to climb trees by digging their claws into the bark. However, older and sometimes very large grizzlies will climb trees if there are branches they can step on like rungs on a ladder. I have observed grizzlies, facilitated by ladder-limbs, eating pinecones high in whitebark pines.

Why do bears climb trees? There appear to be many reasons. Mother bears order cubs to climb trees for safety. The mother bear signals the cubs with an audible "woof," and the urgency of the "woof" tells the cubs how fast and how high to climb. A danger-signal "woof" sends them to the highest points very fast. A mild woof may order the cubs to climb to safe positions so mom can go away to feed. High in the trees, cubs drape across branches and fall asleep. Young bears will remain in trees for hours, waiting for mom's return.

Older bears may also climb for reasons of safety, such as to avoid the charge of a bigger bear or because a person is approaching. Bears often lie on a branch and watch unknowing people walk below.

Black bears in the eastern U.S. build nests high in the forks of trees for use as day beds. In Colorado, black bears have been observed high in aspen trees in the spring, eating new buds. The buds may provide concentrated sources of energy or simply be a flavorful "candy" for the bears. I have not observed either of these behaviors in Yellowstone.

Another way bears mark trees is by rubbing against them to scratch their heavy fur coats. At a given time, rubbing may serve any of three purposes: relief from itching, removal of shed fur, or simply because it feels good. Certainly in the spring, following emergence

Bears like this brown-phase black bear will stand and rub against trees. Rubbing may have multiple functions including scratching, scent marking, or fur removal. It may also simply feel good.

*Rubbing trees (**LEFT**) are often prominent elements of the landscape. Such trees may be larger than average, located near a trail or at the junction of trails, or simply different from surrounding trees. Bears may visit the same tree year after year. Prominent trees also serve as sleeping and baby-sitting platforms for black bear cubs and adults (**RIGHT**).*

from hibernation, rubbing may help remove last year's fur that is coming loose at the roots.

Good rubbing trees, usually conifers, are used over and over again for decades, perhaps even centuries. In the spring before significant new plant growth obscures it, a trail of bear footprints may lead to a favorite tree. Year after year, bears step in the same places when they approach the rubbing tree, creating slight depressions with compressed soil. Next to the tree, twin depressions in the ground show where bears stand on their hind feet while rubbing their backs and stomachs up and down the trunk.

The bark where bears rub will be worn smooth. Rubbing often damages some of the bark, and sap may ooze from openings. Fur may be stuck in the sap and caught on rough edges of the bark. White tips on such hairs indicate a grizzly, but even black fur will bleach to a light, whitish-brown color in a short time.

While rubbing can provide physical benefits to the bear, it is possible that rubbing trees also serve as bulletin boards, places where bears learn about other bears in the area. Multiple bears use the trees each year, and a bear's keen nose may tell it who has rubbed against the tree and when.

Bears leave tooth marks on trees when they feed on cambium, the inner bark. The cambium is nutritious and sweet. Bears will rip loose the bark and then scrape the inner wood with their front teeth. When sap is running down the tree, bears will repeatedly return to eat it. Bears are so enthusiastic about this food that they will sometimes tear off the bark all around a tree, which eventually kills it.

Bears also just bite trees. Their canine teeth leave distinctive holes and scratches. Bears bite from different body positions: standing on all fours and standing on two legs, both facing the tree and with their backs to it. Biting with their backs to a tree is often done while scratching.

Sometimes bears bite off the tops of small saplings, especially near the edges of meadows where they are feeding. Smaller saplings are simply bitten while the bear stands on four legs. Larger trees may be pulled down and sideways with the front feet to facilitate the bite.

The hypothesis that bears mark trees to communicate with other bears is controversial. Bears do not mark and defend a territory like wolves, but one set of hypotheses deals with possessiveness. The story goes that the first bear on the scene reaches as high as possible on a tree and claws the trunk. Other bears that stand against the same tree might decline to leave their mark if they are smaller in

HOW TO READ BEAR TREES

Using only keen observation and a ruler, you can decipher the stories told by bear trees. Bear art trees betray the artist's size and often its age. First, measure the width across the centers of five hind claws. In fresh marks, widths greater than five inches indicate a very large adult bear, probably a grizzly. Second, measure the stride of the bear, the vertical distance from where a claw mark occurs to where the same claw again cuts the bark. The stride approximates the distance from the center of the hip to the center of the shoulder of the bear and identifies the maker as a cub-of-the-year (if less than 20 inches), a yearling (between 20 and 40 inches), or an adult (greater than 40 inches).

Remember, tree trunks get larger each year as trees grow, so the width across five hind claws grows wider with each passing year. If the claw marks appear fresh, the measurement may be reliable. If the claw marks look old with considerable scarring of the bark, the track size may be exaggerated by years of growth. Then it is better to use stride as an indicator of bear size.

The height of tooth marks also reveals bear size. Since a bear cannot bite a flat surface, it must turn its head sideways to bite the trunk. The teeth marks from the upper jaw will be slightly higher than the marks from the lower jaw. Stand and face a tree trunk and try it yourself. Understanding the process allows you to estimate the height of a bear. Remember to add additional inches above the tooth marks to estimate the height of the bear's head if it were standing straight. Tooth marks that are six feet or more above the ground indicate a big bear!

When a bear bites, whichever set of canine teeth, uppers or lowers, locks into the wood first serves as an anchor and the other teeth are pulled towards the anchor. This creates tooth drag marks.

When you measure, make sure you have a single bite and not parts of two bites; a measurable bite shows all four canines.

The distance from the center of one canine tooth mark to the center of the other canine tooth mark helps identify the species. Canines in the upper jaw are generally wider spaced than canines in the lower jaw. Canine separation for black bears is 1.7 to 2.2 inches (upper jaw) by 1.4 to 2.1 inches (lower jaw), and for grizzlies bears is 1.9 to 3.5 inches (upper jaw) by 1.4 to 3.0 inches (lower jaw).

Bears often rip open downed logs to obtain insects. However, old logs also fall apart from other natural processes. To determine if a bear tore open the log, look for claw marks around the edges of the opening in the log. Claw marks may be difficult to find because hard dead wood is not easily marked. For additional verification that a bear was feeding, look for large pieces of wood torn from the log, especially any pieces that lie uphill from the log. Those pieces must have been thrown there, probably by a bear. To age the event, look under the pieces of the log that have been scattered on the ground. Yellowing of plants under the pieces means the log was torn open days earlier. If, when a piece is moved, the grass underneath springs upright, it is very fresh so be bear aware.

Bear footprints are recorded as claw marks in aspen bark. The horizontal arcs of claw points represent hind claws while the longer vertical scratches are made by front claws.

size. Since grizzlies do bite prominent trees in their range, perhaps the bite marks do communicate possessiveness or size to other bears.

Since a bear is a "nose on four legs," information on tree need not be about possession but simply about what bear has passed that way and how recently. If a young male is wandering near a large old male, this information might be important.

From decades of observation, there is no doubt in my mind that bears glean information from marked trees. As sensory-challenged humans who especially lack an acute sense of smell, we should be careful not to underestimate the information on a bear tree.

Tracks

Bears have five toes on each foot, but the little toe may not show in a poorly formed track, or on hard ground, or in a trail created by the

The Palmisciano method for differentiating black & grizzly tracks

Black Bear Track
Right front track

Grizzly Bear Track
Right front track

1. Anchor the line to the posterior point of the outside (largest) toe
2. Align with the anterior point of interdigital (palm) pad
3. Test where the line intersects the inside (smallest) toe
   if more than half the toe is anterior to the line, it is a grizzly bear track
   if more than half the toe is posterior to the line, it is a black bear track

The arc of toes of the grizzly track is flatter than that of the black bear track.

bear moving fast. Unlike people, the big toe of a bear foot is on the outside of the foot. Claws often show in black bear tracks and usually show in grizzly tracks, but not always.

Telling black bear tracks from grizzly tracks is not always easy. Anyone who says it is has not done much tracking. The "classic" grizzly track shows claws that are 1.5 to 2 times longer than the length of their corresponding toes. This is great guideline, but a grizzly that has been digging a lot will have short claws (worn down by the digging) and the claws may not even show in a footprint.

Trackers use other clues when claw marks do not provide definitive identification. Foot anatomy provides important distinctions. All mammals have webbed feet. Feel between your fingers to see how much webbing you have. In grizzlies, the webbing of the front foot extends halfway to the tip of the toes. In black bears the webbing of the front foot extends only 10 percent of the way to the tips of the toes. Webbing shows in a track where the toes splay apart slightly.

The late Dan Palmisciano, a Montana Fish Wildlife and Parks biologist, championed an identification test based on the front footprint. Take a ruler or knife and touch (anchor) the edge to the big toe. Next align the straight edge with the top of the interdigital pad and see where it crosses the imprint of the little toe. A grizzly has a rather straight arrangement of toes and the straight edge will intersect the posterior half of the little toe. In black bear tracks, the line will intersect the anterior half of the little toe. This test is for the front foot only. If you have a good, clean track, it is very accurate. (*See diagram, left*)

Few fail to be impressed with the size of a bear track, especially that of a large male grizzly. But only trackers recognize the visual exaggeration caused by a soft surface like mud. Place your hand on a flat table. Feel the cool area of contact. That is the true size of your

hand print, known as the minimum outline. Now imagine your hand pressing into soft mud. As your hand sinks deeper, the mud flows out and away from your fingers, and the hand print increases in size. This is a visual exaggeration of the true size of your hand. So trackers measure the minimum outline, or the edge in the bottom of the track, not the upper exaggerated edge. Next time someone brags about a big bear track they saw, ascertain if the track was in mud or another soft material.

Here are true track sizes measured in Yellowstone: The front feet of adult female grizzlies measure from 4.5 to 5 inches long by a little more than 5 inches wide. The front feet of adult male grizzlies measure from 4.5 to 6 inches long by 5 to 7 inches wide.

The hind feet of adult female grizzlies measure from 7.5 to 9.5 inches long by 4.5 to 5.5 inches wide. The hind feet of adult male grizzlies measure from 7 to 10 inches long by 4.5 to 5.5 inches wide.

The front feet of adult black bears measure from 3.5 to 4.5 inches long by 4.5 to 5.5 inches wide, and the hind feet of adult black bears measure about 7 inches long by 4 inches wide.

Traveling bears typically use a fast shuffling gait known as an amble. The hind foot touches the ground forward of the front foot, and the faster the amble the further forward the hind foot lands. The average stride (measured from a point of a foot striking the ground to the same point striking the ground again) of a walking grizzly varies from 35 to 55 inches. Black bears have shorter strides. Bears often lope, leaving a pattern of four prints that form the shape of a

Reading the trail of this bear reveals information to a tracker. Long claws on the front foot (second from the bottom) identify the bear as a grizzly. Footprint size indicates a large adult. The hind foot overstepped (landed in front of) the front foot on the same side, indicating the grizzly was traveling at a fast walk known as an amble.

"C" (or a reversed "C") with a stride of 40 to 50 inches. At a full-speed gallop, a grizzly's stride is easily more than 15 feet. When rapidly climbing a hill, bears bound with the hind feet placed beside each other.

Bears sometimes create trails by using the same paths for hundreds of years. Deep depressions define where each foot is placed. While such trails are rare in Yellowstone, look for them on narrow passes in the mountains, leading to trout streams, and at bear rub trees.

Feeding signs

Bears leave signs while feeding, including "flips" and "digs." "Flips" are objects rolled or turned over by bears with their front feet. They include scat of other mammals, rocks, and logs.

A few hours turning over and tearing apart scat can provide a great nutritional living for a grizzly. Bison pies or scat trap moisture and provide thermal insulation for earthworms. On cold spring mornings when frost covers the ground, grizzlies will flip scats to obtain large masses of warm earthworms. A few pie flips can provide

A female grizzly walks down a hillside, testing the soil and looking for tubers to dig.

The author investigates a "gopher dig" where a grizzly moved considerable dirt to expose the gopher's food cache and perhaps even catch the gopher itself.

several pounds of earthworms. Later in the summer bears find a plethora of insects and insect larvae inside and beneath scat.

Flipping rocks also provides a source of insects and their larvae. While bears frequent meadows and flip a few rocks there, rock flipping really pays off in the alpine tundra where army cutworm moths congregate under boulders. Bears may move Volkswagen-sized boulders to get to the moths. They grab boulders with their front feet and, using gravity, roll them downhill. Digging down to the frost line generates a reward of pounds of moths.

Bears, especially grizzlies, dig for many food sources including roots, insects, small mammals, and food caches. The evidence left by digging for plants may be minute or massive. In the spring grizzlies dig for spring beauties by deftly inserting their long claws next to a plant. They rotate the claws and pull up, neatly extracting the plant, bulb and all. The "divot" thus created may be less than an inch in diameter. A field may contain hundreds of divots, but to the untrained eye they go undetected. At other times where a grizzly has dug for bistort and biscuit root, a hillside may look like it's been tilled with machinery.

Large excavations are usually associated with pocket gophers: their tunnels, nests, and food caches. The pocket gopher, a small rodent weighing about one-quarter of a pound, does not hibernate but spends all winter beneath the ground and snow, excavating roots and placing them in chambers in the snow or just below the ground. A cache may be larger than a basketball and represents a significant food source for the bears. Bears go to great lengths to dig outs these caches, sometimes eating a hapless gopher in the process.

In the fall during hyperphagia, grizzlies will move many square yards of dirt to get at small mammals, including ground squirrels, pocket gophers, voles, and packrats. Highest on their preference list is the ground squirrel. Of the small mammals mentioned, only the ground squirrel hibernates, so by fall it has accumulated body fat. Perhaps the abundance of fat triggers a special longing in the grizzly because bears seem to expend far more energy digging for ground squirrels than can be realized from the rodents themselves. But perhaps there is more energy in ground squirrels than we realize.

Grizzlies are the major diggers. Black bears seldom dig plants, mammals, or rodent caches. However, when it comes to ants, even black bears go wild. Both species will decapitate ant mounds, the round inverted cones so diligently formed by certain species of ants, and both species dig deep into the ground to expose the labyrinth of ant chambers. Using either a lap of the tongue or the rake of a forefoot, scads of ants are scooped into the bear's mouth.

To a scatologist, bear feces contain a wealth of information. Color, odor, and food remnants reveal what was eaten. Diameter hints at the size of the bear and the quantity of available food. Moisture content tells how long ago the bear was there.

Scat

Bear scat provides information about the bear and its diet. In the laboratory using DNA, chemical, and hormonal tests on scat, it is possible to identify gender, reproduction status, and nutritional condition. Even in the field scat provides detailed information.

Bear scat appears human-like. Usually the scat consists of a large pile with many short cords. Cords are large in diameter with blunt to slightly tapering ends.

Bear scat varies with what was eaten, especially with the food's fiber and moisture content. Fiber and moisture control scat diameter, which provides a strong clue as to the species of the bear.

Moist scat from dining on food items such as pin cherry or huckleberries will form small diameter cords. A fibrous diet of whitebark pine nuts will produce large diameter cords. A fibrous and moist diet of spring grasses produces small diameter cords but large piles. A very rich diet of fresh meat may cause a scat to be a "cow pie," semi-liquid with almost no shape. A diet of moths will produce small cords and small piles.

To determine the identity of the scat maker, measure the greatest diameter of a non-flattened cord. If the cord is 1.5 inches or larger in diameter, consider the maker to be a grizzly. This will be correct about 70 percent of the time. A secondary clue to improve scat identification is quantity; larger quantities probably come from grizzlies.

Odor, color, and contents provide other clues. Scat composed of grass are very sweet smelling, even more than those derived from berries. Berry scat, incidently, may be blue or purple. Scat from a meat diet stinks. A high percentage of fur and bone fragments in the scat indicates feeding on an old carcass without much meat left on it. Bits of woody material in bear scat reveals a diet of whitebark pine nuts. Moth wings reveal feeding at an alpine site, fish scales indicate a diet of spawning trout, and ant heads reveal a raid on an ant mound.

Bear scat, in turn, provides food for others in Yellowstone. The semi-liquid "cow pie" scat derived from fresh meat retains considerable animal protein. Insects quickly devour meat scats, hiding their prevalence from scientists. Dung beetles roll balls of dung to holes they have made in the ground. Safely deposited in the hole, beetles lay their eggs in the dung so the beetles' developing larvae can devour the scat as they grow.

Beds

Bears sleep at night and during the hot part of the day. Before they sleep, bears may construct "beds" of varying structures. Beds are often located just inside the forest along the edge of grass meadows. Rooms with a view serve as lookouts for anyone or anything that might approach during their slumber. It is a wise hiker who walks far out in an open meadow and not along the forest edge, thereby providing any bears in nearby beds the opportunity to sense the hiker's approach and quietly slip deeper into the forest.

Beds are often on the uphill side of a large conifer. They may consist of a simple scooped out depression in the duff (woody debris). Branches may be broken off on the side of the tree the bear sleeps against. When temperatures are hot, bears will often make deep depressions in the soil, perhaps to use the cool earth to dissipate

their own body heat. These deep depressions are often found in dense shaded forest or underbrush. Deep beds may be used for several days in a row. Bears occasionally drag branches or small vegetation into their beds.

When beds are used for several days, scat tends to accumulate near the bed. Trails may lead to the best bed sites. One such bed site made me a hero in the eyes of the Yellowstone National Park Interpretive Division, well, at least for awhile. My friend George Robinson, then head of Interpretation, invited me to teach a tracking and field seminar for summer staff. We met at the YAC camp south of Mammoth. I hadn't had time to scout the area because I had arrived by plane from Colorado only an hour before the class started.

Following my lecture, I took the group outside and started to walk up the dust-covered dirt road to Bunsen Peak. I spotted black bear tracks crossing the road and the fragile tracks in the dust still showed moisture on their exposed edges. I quieted the crowd with a finger to my lips and by charades conveyed the idea that this was a fresh bear trail. Next I indicated to my skeptical audience that we would follow the trail and maybe see the bear. Stalking quietly, we headed into the forest.

Scanning ahead 50 yards, I suddenly spotted the ears of a bear above and behind a downed log. Then the head appeared. Then the head disappeared. We backed away, circled, and gained some higher ground to look at the log. There was a cinnamon-colored black bear stretched out on its back. It had scooped out a bed in a decayed log.

The bear threw a front leg out to the side and looked up to see if any intruders were present. Our group was stone silent. No one moved. Then the bear threw a hind leg out to the side and repeated its scan. Next, the other front leg went to the side. Initially the bear made scans every 30 seconds or so. Then it scanned every minute, and then every two minutes as it drifted off to sleep. The bear just wanted to be cool on the hot summer day and left alone. One-by-one my group retreated, believing I was the greatest tracker in the world because I had just led them to a bear in its bed only 300 yards from our classroom. Sometimes luck is a wonderful thing.

Hair

Bears often leave hairs on rubbing spots, fences, and their beds. While definitive hair analysis requires high quality microscopes, many clues may be ascertained by looking carefully at the hair, especially if a hand lens is available. A six-inch ruler also helps.

Mammals have two types of hairs: long, thick hairs known as guard hairs and shorter, often very fine hairs known as fur or wool. Most identification is based on the guard hairs. Each hair consists of a central portion known as the medulla and an outer portion known as the cortex. The internal structure of the medulla and cortex are differentiated by cell shape, but cell shape is only visible under a microscope. Pigments may be found in different portions of the hair.

When looking at a hair, determine if it has a root (small visible bulb) at one end and is tapered at the other end. If it doesn't, you have a broken hair and will have to allow for a longer length when you measure it. Grizzly guard hairs are generally rich brown to black, often with light brown or silver tips. Their average length varies from 2.5 inches to more than 3 inches. The diameter of each hair is thick.

Black bear guard hairs vary in color from yellowish to reddish to brown to black. Average length seldom exceeds two inches. The diameter of each hair is relatively thin. Bear fur consists of smooth, wavy, very thin hairs. All hairs are uniformly colored with no distinctive bands.

Hairs are often easy to find on rub trees, but most rub trees in Yellowstone are made by bison. Bison leave hair which can look very

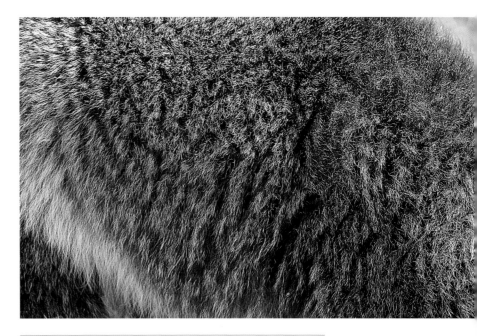

The color and pattern of bear fur identifies species and marks individuals. This is grizzly fur. Fur is shed each spring and increases in thickness during the fall to provide winter insulation. Fur also protects the skin from cuts, bites, and abrasions.

similar to bear hair. If you find a silver-tipped hair, it is a grizzly. But if the silver tip is absent, distinguishing grizzly and bison hair can be difficult. Bison hairs are often very long and the fur may be more sharply undulating that bear hair. Look at the hair through a hand lens. The medulla of bison hair is broken and spans more than half the width of the hair, while the medulla of the bear hair is continuous, distinct, and less than half the width of the hair.

Hair from other ungulates may be found on rubs, but it will be thick, brittle hair with sharp undulations. Lay a hair against a seam on your shirt to check for undulations. Break a hair to see if it feels brittle and breaks easy. If it does, it's ungulate hair.

III. ECOLOGY

1. FOODS AND FEEDING HABITS

Our knowledge of bear food availability and its usage is critical to understanding the number and distribution of bears and to predicting and managing their future. This is especially true as food sources in the Greater Yellowstone Ecosystem are affected by human population growth, climate change, drought, wild fire, exotic species, insect infestations, and animal diseases. Techniques for studying bear diets have steadily improved, but we remain far short of complete understanding.

Some bear food items are mundane, some unexpected, and some delve into the realm of exotic. I am indebted to Dave Mattson for sharing research and insights into many diet items, especially the lesser known. Dave and many colleagues from the Interagency Grizzly Bear Study Team made a monumental effort to study the diet of bears. Between 1977 and 1996 they collected more than 7,000 scats from more than 2,000 radio-telemetry locations of at least 175 radio-collared bears. Feeding signs were documented at more than 3,000 sites. Since 1996, many additional hours, days, and months of laboratory study have been conducted. I am indebted to Kerry Gunther, Charles Schwartz, Mark Haroldson, and Lisette Waits for sharing additional information.

A subadult male grizzly shows the dexterity of its toes by holding and eating a root. Knowledge of bear foods is crucial to protecting bear habitat and managing bears.

Scat Analysis

Direct observation of wild foraging bears is difficult, time consuming, and fraught with limitations such as, but not limited to, following bears at night. The obvious alternative is to examine bear scat. This sounds simple but problems exist. Scat shows what is excreted, not what is eaten. Scat content and dietary information are not the same thing. Researchers must consider the nutritional value of individual foods, seasonal importance, availability, and many other factors to better understand what bears eat and why they eat certain foods.

For example, if 170 different scats contained ants and 72 scats contained grass, are ants more important than grass? By these numbers it may seem so, but a second indicator of dietary importance is volume. By volume, ants may only make up one percent of scat while grass makes up 99 percent. Frequency and volume together expand our knowledge of the importance of food items, but there is yet another factor: digestibility.

In analyzing scat content over an entire year, meat appears to be relatively scarce and unimportant. This is a false impression because highly digestible foods are under-represented. For example, high-fiber grass will yield voluminous scat while highly nutritious meat is mostly digested and yields a small volume of scat. Additionally, scat containing meat residue is quickly eaten by insects so it may not be found by researchers.

Yet another variable is caloric content. Which foods provide the most calories? Obviously this work is complex, and the intricate details are beyond the scope of this book. However, what follows below are some findings summarized for the bears of Yellowstone. I am indebted to Steve Mealey, bear biologist and early mentor of mine, and other researchers for this information.

In terms of calories per gram of food, trout ranked highest at 5.7 calories per gram, followed by elk at 5.6, whitebark pine nuts 4.0, springbeauties 4.0, grasses 3.3, clover 3.6, and horsetails 2.9. For reference, there are about 9.3 calories per gram in fat, 3.8 in carbohydrates, and 3.1 in proteins. Interestingly, human garbage averages about 3.4 calories per gram, which helps explain why bears are so attracted to garbage.

In terms of digestibility, elk and trout were the most digestible, 81 percent and 73 percent respectively, thus yielding low amounts of residue in scat. Other digestibility values are whitebark pine nuts at 49 percent, springbeauties 31 percent, grasses 16 percent, clover 14 percent, and horsetails 13 percent.

Of course, not all food items are distributed equally across the park, and bears concentrate when and where food resources are high. Unproductive lands receive less attention from bears. Bear scat in different geographic areas provides insight into how bears use their

food supplies. Each area has a "feeding economy" which represents the energy bank account available to bears in those areas. In Yellowstone, these "feeding economies" were designated Valley/Plateau, Mountain, and Lake.

Using a mathematical formula incorporating frequency, volume, caloric value, and digestibility of food items found in scat, Mealey found that when grizzlies were in the Mountain economy they concentrated on springbeauties and secondarily on graminoids (grasses and grass-like plants). In the Valley/Plateau economy, graminoids were dominant. In the Lake economy, graminoids shared the spotlight with cutthroat trout while thistles and horsetails shared a secondary role.

Each economy had a unique nutritional characteristic. For the Valley/Plateau economy it was protein from succulent herbs. For the Mountain economy it was starch from roots. For the Lake economy it was protein and fat from fish. Protein from succulent herbs was the primary nutrient in all three economies.

Scat volume analysis provided what I call the standard scat year, a comparative picture of food utilization by grizzlies in the GYE. Food items collected in scat from 1977 to 1987 were averaged to create a picture of the "standard" seasonal usage by grizzlies. By comparison with this "standard" year, scat collections since then have provided insights into changing food habits.

It is instructive to compare the diets of Yellowstone grizzlies to the diets of bears in other regions. In all other areas, berries are a very important part of the diet. In the GYE however, bears obtain little nutritive value from berries because of the relative scarcity of

A male black bear dines on the Valley/Plateau feeding economy. Grasses and herbs form the nutritional basis of lush meadows.

berries. In the GYE whitebark pine nuts have replaced berries, although in other ecosystems the nuts are of less value.

Detailed studies of bear diets in the GYE reveal interesting changes in the proportion of meat to plants over time. For black bears and grizzlies, isotopes of carbon, nitrogen, and sulphur from bone and hair samples collected from museums and dating from the first two decades of the 20th century were compared to blood, bone, and hair samples collected from bears since 1977. These studies were done by Grant Hilderbrand, Michael Jacoby and their colleagues.

In the early 20th century, the diet of female grizzlies was 72 percent meat and 28 percent plants, while that of male grizzlies was 98 percent meat. The proportion of meat in modern grizzly diets was: subadult females 45 percent, adult females 45 percent, subadult males 37 percent, and adult males 79 percent. The high proportion of meat in the historic diet may reflect greater availability of livestock at the time. Two modern males and two modern females removed from the GYE because of predation on livestock had meat proportions of 83 and 86 percent respectively. It also appears that at least some males in Yellowstone concentrate on obtaining meat.

As a side note, the proportion of meat in the diet of grizzlies in Glacier National Park is only 33 percent for males and zero percent for females! Meat is less available in the Glacier ecosystem, and greater annual precipitation results in a high production of berries. Glacier grizzlies rely heavily on the sweets.

Far less data are available on black bear diets in the GYE. Of course black bears and grizzly bears eat many of the same things but the proportions are different. Notably, roots, bulbs, and corms are lacking from the diet of black bears because black bears dig less for food. So it is not surprising that black bears receive little nutritive value from plant structures below ground. There is also a corresponding lack of ground debris in black bear scat, probably for the same reasons.

Historically black bear females had a meat proportion of 54 percent compared to all modern black bears with a meat proportion of 41 percent. Again the reduction in meat over time is apparent, perhaps for the same reason as grizzlies. Overall the diet of black bears reflects a more herbivorous nature than grizzlies.

Geophagy

Geophagy is "scientificese" for eating dirt. One example is the use of mineral licks by ungulates. Primates, including humans, ingest

To humans, dirt is a strange component of a bear's diet. Dirt may serve as an anti-diarrheal medication, a nutrient supplement, or a parasiticide. Here a black bear mother and cub cross a dirt site in a thermal area.

soil to supplement minerals such as iron, copper, potassium, calcium, zinc, and manganese. We also use "dirt" for anti-diarrhea treatments, to counter toxins, and for medicines against intestinal parasites.

Mattson found bear geophagy sites associated with Yellowstone thermal areas. The sites smelled sulphurous. Geophagy sites differed from mineral licks by having high amounts of potassium, sodium, and magnesium and, to a certain extent, sulphur. Well-worn bear trails led to some sites. Claw marks revealed that bears dug depressions to lie in the odorous earth. Apparent purposeful ingestion of soil peaked from March through May and secondarily in August through October.

To date, geophagy raises more questions than answers. It is possible that bears ingest soils as an anti-diarrheal, and the soils need to be analyzed for therapeutic clay minerals. It does not appear that ingested soil helps to detoxify plant toxins. It is possible that potassium and magnesium provide needed nutrition and that sulphur acts as a parasiticide or fungicide. Anaerobic bacteria in the intestine may facilitate digestion by fermentation of fiber. If these bacteria die during the winter, then eating soil may provide a new crop each spring.

I have observed black and grizzly bears using these sites, and all were males. But never have I observed them actually eating the soil. Most actions I saw involved rubbing in the soil. Since the rolling occurred during the breeding season, I wonder if it might be an attempt to enhance the odor of a dominant male.

Truffles and mushrooms

Nutritionally it makes sense to eat sporocarps (fruiting bodies), which we call truffles and mushrooms. Sporocarps contain four to six calories per gram and are highly digestible.

Verifying the tastes of human mushroom lovers, bears eat false truffles, gilled mushrooms, boletes, and morels. Interestingly, bears

Most of time bears like this grizzly act as lawn mowers on four legs, clipping green grass to add to their caloric consumption.

dug deeper for false truffles but excavated the same amount of soil as for mushrooms.

Sporocarp feeding occurs mostly in August, September, and October and is highest in September. Bears rarely feed on fungi before July. Autumn is when the bear's favorite fungi become available in the preferred habitat: lodgepole pine forests with sparse ground cover.

Given the nutritional value of fungi and their wide distribution in the GYE, it is surprising that bears do not feed more on sporocarps. Only one percent of analyzed scat and two percent of visited feeding sites showed that bears were eating mushrooms and truffles.

While sporocarp consumption is low, it may increase in the future. Climate models suggest that warming temperatures may favor the spread of lodgepole pine forests, increasing mushroom feeding areas.

Plants

The teeth of a carnivore are shaped to slice. The last upper premolar and the lower first molar, together called the carnassial pair, are vertically elongate so they slide past each other like the blades of scissors. A carnassial pair is the hallmark of a carnivore, and many people are surprised to learn that bears do not possess the slicing carnassial pair. The reason is that bears do not specialize on meat; they eat almost anything. Such a varied menu makes bears omnivores.

Bear cheek teeth, like our teeth, have rounded cusps. Rounded cusps allow bears to chew pine nut shells, squash ants, and grind grass. In fact, bears are so attuned to eating grass they might be better described as herbivores with occasional predation.

Plant usage is dependent on many factors. A plant that is eaten in one geographic region may not be used in another area. Use depends on abundance, other plant species present, and the energy required obtaining the food. Use patterns change as plants mature. For example, the digestibility of grasses drops from 34 percent in the spring to 32 percent during the breeding season to 18 percent in the summer to 13 percent in hyperphagia—prompting bears to focus on other foods in the fall.

Springbeauties are key plants in the spring when most foods are scarce. The entire plant is edible and lush growth of the plant on wet hillsides provides a wealth of food. Grizzlies begin digging the roots as soon as the snow melts. However, springbeauties quickly disappear

Springbeauties are a key element of the Mountain feeding economy. The entire plant is edible. The flower tastes sweet but the most nutritious part is the root, which has a pleasant potato-like flavor.

ABOVE: *During the summer when grass shoots are young, sweet, and nutritious, bears like this black bear spend exorbitant amounts of time grazing.*

RIGHT: *Once berries and fruits ripen, bears turn their attentions to sweeter rewards. Here a brown-phase black bear dines on rose hips.*

with the coming of summer. Roots of yampah and biscuitroot are highly nutritious and available all summer. Grass and grass-like plants provide easily accessible food sources but their nutritional values decrease as plants dry out in the summer. Clover and other flowering plants reach their apex later in the summer and are available into hyperphagia. Thistle provides a large amount of food for the effort but its spines may reduce its value. Horsetails, while providing low nutritional content, seem to be favored. Horsetails may provide a cleansing effect as they pass through the digestive tract, helping remove internal parasites.

As noted earlier, berries do not play a large role in the diet of GYE bears because few berries are produced in the area's dry climate. In addition, large numbers of ungulates have devastated ground-growing berries in many areas. Berries provide less than one percent of the annual nutrition in the diet of GYE bears.

When there is a summer with poor berry production, local people often say bears come out of the mountains into developed areas looking for food. A "bad berry year" is the result of low precipitation. Of course, lacking moisture all forage plants dry out early in the season. It is the lower nutritional value in all vegetation, not just the lack of berries, that forces bears to search for substitute foods.

Plants may also vary in their food potential from year to year and even in longer cycles. For example, in the summer of 1986 Mattson discovered that bears all across the ecosystem were avidly digging the roots of sweet-cicely, a previously minor or unused plant. Tests showed that sweet-cicely roots that year contained more starch and were more digestible than in previous years. Use of sweet-cicely tapered off to almost zero over the next two years. Perhaps precipitation patterns led to the high starch content that one year.

Mattson pointed out that bears pay close attention to the world they live in and sample many possible foods day after day. We should not be surprised that bears possess the ability to quickly discover and utilize new or different foods.

Whitebark pine

One plant food in the GYE is critical beyond all others: whitebark pine nuts. The whitebark pine is a stone pine, and there are three stone pines common in the Rocky Mountains: whitebark pine, limber pine, and pinyon pine. All three share a common characteristic: their

Whitebark pine trees produce cones approximately every three or four years. The seeds or nuts are nutritious and form an important food source for Yellowstone bears during their hyperphagia phase of fattening up for hibernation.

large edible nuts are full of triacerglycerol, a substance that provides energy comparable to fleshy fruits like berries.

Whitebark pine nuts are important to many animals. Clark's nutcrackers (*Nucifragas columbiana*) are birds that rely on pine nuts for food. They use their long, powerful beaks to extract the nuts from the cones. In addition to eating the nuts on the spot, nutcrackers pack large numbers of nuts into throat pouches just below their tongues. Then they fly to remote, warm, south-facing sites to cache the nuts in the ground for winter food. A single bird may make 2000 caches in one autumn. Diana Tombeck tells me that her testing shows that the birds remember the location of every cache.

During a mild winter, nutcrackers do not retrieve every nut from their caches, and nuts left in the ground may sprout. The average

number of nuts in a cache is five, and whitebark pines are often found growing with about five stems per site. In this way nutcrackers disperse and plant whitebark pine nuts. The relationship is mutualistic: whitebark pines need nutcrackers and nutcrackers need whitebark pines.

Red squirrels take advantage of whitebark pine nuts by caching both cones and nuts. Kate Kendall's early studies showed that squirrels begin caching cones the first week of August, placing them in holes from one to four inches deep in a midden. Middens are mounds or large piles of old cones built by red squirrels. Many middens are used for years. A single midden may contain 3,000 cones. Middens are moist and wet in their interiors, and moist, wet cones do not open so the nuts remain in the cones for the squirrel to retrieve later, even from under winter snows. In low cone production years, almost all cones that are produced are buried in middens. During years of high cone production, squirrels may simply leave hundreds

of cones on top of middens. In mid-September squirrels switch to caching pine nuts. Nut caches may contain five to 175 nuts each.

Both grizzlies and black bears eat pine nuts. Nuts may be obtained in several ways. Bears find cones on the ground beneath trees, strip cones from branches, or climb trees for the cones, but by far the most common method is raiding squirrel middens. Evidently bears can locate middens by smell. Black and grizzly bears commonly feed at the same middens.

Once in the Absaroka Mountains northeast of Cooke City I watched a female grizzly and her two yearlings climb 20 feet up the sprawling branches of a whitebark pine. Sometimes she broke off branches with cones, other times she stripped cones from the branches with her claws, and occasionally she ate cones while in the tree. Back on the ground she retrieved the cones for herself. When I later investigated the tree, the number of broken branches indicated she had visited it more than once.

In general, grizzlies are delicate about extracting the nuts. They will crush a cone with a paw and then spread out the crushed material. They pick up the nuts by placing their tongue on them. I have witnessed grizzlies carefully using their long claws to separate nuts from other parts of the cone for easier eating. A crushing bite fractures the nut coat, exposing the nutritionally rich seed. By extracting the nuts, bears avoid passing hard, low-nutrition cone scales through their digestive tracts. The resulting scat contains mostly nut coats. Few nuts pass through intact, so bears do not serve as the main nut dispensers.

Occasionally bears do eat the entire cones, and Chuck Jonkel tells me that when bears eat the entire cone, they gain additional subsistence from the fleshy pulp of the cone.

Whitebark pines grow mostly at elevations above 8,500 feet and cone production varies from year to year. A good year with high production occurs about every six years. Low production years are relatively common, occurring about every two years, and production may be nearly zero in some years. Cone production also varies from one area to another.

In a good cone year bear usage is high in the fall and the following spring. Exceptionally good years may provide cones for use into the second summer. Only in years of abundant limber pine cone production do bears make much use of limber pines, the whitebark's biological cousin in the GYE. This may be because limber pine nuts fall out of their cones, so building large caches of single nuts may require too much effort by the red squirrels. Black bears appear to be the main species eating limber pine nuts.

The highly digestible lipid content of pine nuts provides an

FACING PAGE: *When whitebark pine cones are especially abundant, red squirrels sometimes simply pile up extra cones on top of their middens instead of burying them. Grizzly bears raid red squirrel middens for the nuts in the pine cones.*

important way of quickly adding fat in preparation for hibernation. In good cone years bears feed on pine nuts almost to the exclusion of other foods. Conversely, during poor cone years, bears often wander far from secure mountain retreats, and the number of bear/human conflicts during hyperphagia is substantially higher. Mortality of female bears outside of the park is higher during poor cone years.

Ecologist Laura Felicetti delineated grizzly usage of pine nuts with stable isotopes. Since the balance of sulfur and nitrogen is characteristically different in pine nuts compared to other plants, moths, ungulates, and trout, scientists were able to determine the amount of each bear's diet derived from pine nuts.

When cone crops were good, bears derived more than half their dietary sulphur and nitrogen from pine nuts. During poor cone years, bears made minimal use of pine nuts. In a good cone year, pine nuts may provide 14 times more energy than meat to the bears that concentrate on them. Nut importance is unequivocal, but when cone crops fail, meat is critical.

Whitebark pines can easily live to be 500 years old. However, they do not produce significant cone crops until they reach about 100 years of age, so cone-producing stands tend to be mature or old-growth forests. Few new trees become established each year.

Because of their limited geographic distribution, the survival of whitebark pine is susceptible to catastrophic events including fire, drought, insect invasion, and climate change. Recently the severity of onslaughts on whitebark pine has caught scientists off guard. Like a one-two punch, blister rust has attacked young trees and bark beetles have attacked mature trees. Fires have taken other healthy trees. A 2003 aerial survey of the GYE detected 150,000 dead whitebark pines, with 11,000 in Yellowstone National Park alone. The spread of the bark beetle infestation since 2003 has been massive (*See sidebar page 72*), and the future of this important food source is uncertain.

Whitebark pines (LEFT) grow at high elevations. Healthy trees produce nuts that are food for many animals, including bears. In recent years, drought, fungus, insect invasions, and fires have taken their toll on all conifers in the Greater Yellowstone Ecosystem. (BELOW) Note the dead trees in the background, including the whitebark pine (the round-shaped conifer in the center of the photo).

JIM HALFPENNY

First came blister rust (Cronartium ribicola), a fungus accidentally introduced into Canada from Europe in the 1920s. The disease quickly spread. In northwest Montana it claimed 90 to 100 percent of whitebark pines. Mortality rates have been lower in the GYE, around 10 percent. The fungus attacks seedlings, saplings, and branches on older trees. Dead and dying branches turn red and trees may take 10 years to die. Perhaps one tree in 10,000 is immune to the fungus.

Blister rust has a two-pronged impact. By killing young trees it severely impacts future population growth. It kills older trees from the top down, and since cones tend to grow on a tree's upper branches, nut production fails before the tree actually dies.

A second onslaught came in the form of fire, particularly the fires of 1988 when about 24 percent of Yellowstone's whitebark pines were killed. GYE is a fire-controlled ecosystem with about 30 fire ignitions per year. Fires since 1988 have taken additional trees.

During the summer of 2005 the long-term drought index indicated that the GYE was experiencing some of the lowest moisture levels in North America. Although droughts have occurred repeatedly in the past, conditions may now be exacerbated by climate change bringing drier weather patterns to the Rocky Mountains.

Low levels of ground moisture are facilitating the third onslaught: mountain pine bark beetles (Dendroctonus ponderosae). The beetles are about the size of a pencil eraser and attack both mature lodgepole and whitebark pines, killing them within one to two years.

The cycle of pine beetle infestation starts in May or June when a female beetle arrives at a tree and bores under the bark. She emits a pheromone,

a sexual hormone which attracts other male and female beetles. Beetles flock to the tree and bore into the bark. Pencil-sized holes, sawdust, and pitch spots on tree trunks are signs of infestation. Normally, healthy trees produce sap which "pitches" out the insects. However, drought-weakened trees lack the moisture to produce enough sap to counter the invasion.

Beetles construct vertical tunnels underneath the bark where they lay eggs. The eggs hatch in a week and the larvae burrow at right angles to the main tunnel. The tunnels disrupt the flow of nutrients in the tree, effectively girdling the tree and killing it. The larvae mature into adults in August and overwinter beneath the bark.

In the winter cold temperatures usually kill beetles, limiting beetle invasions in extent and in elevation. However recent warm winters have allowed beetles to survive over larger areas and at higher elevations.

Roy Renkin, park biologist, explained that pine bark beetle infestations were first reported on Dunraven Pass in 1925. Control efforts failed to stop the infestations but whitebark stands still survived, although many of the older, larger trees succumbed. Sub-mature trees seemed to have the vitality to ward off beetles.

Renkin noted that during major insect infestations of the past, chemical controls were used but proved ineffective. In the Cody Canyon east of the park more than 260,000 gallons of lead arsenate were sprayed on trees. Cattle in the area died from eating grass tainted with the chemical. On the northern range within the park, airplanes sprayed 62 tons of DDT mixed with 125,000 gallons of fuel oil. While forest managers hate to lose trees to insect invasions, I hope our response will never again include such insults on the Greater Yellowstone Ecosystem.

Earthworms

When available, earthworms are eaten by bears. Dave, Steve, and Marilyn French (Yellowstone Grizzly Foundation) identified earthworm-feeding sites in grassy swales with wet soils, usually from poor drainage or melt water from nearby snowbanks. Feeding sites were "moderately deep excavations in sod or mud." Worm feeding peaked during the last two weeks of April and the first two weeks of May. While feeding, bears flipped out clumps of dirt and extracted worms with their lips and tongues. The French's estimated about 150 worms per square yard or as many as 8,000 worms for an entire feeding site.

I have observed grizzlies feeding on worms in moist grassy areas by turning over bison paddies. Beneath each paddy was a nearly solid mass of earthworms. I have even seen this behavior when there was a coating of frost on each paddy. Investigating, I turned over several paddies and found a warmer environment with temperatures well above freezing. The earthworms were quite active. I have also observed grizzlies pulling worms out of moist soil in swale bottoms, one worm at a time.

One way grizzly bears feed on earthworms is by turning over bison paddies, particularly on cold spring days when dozens of worms can be found under a single paddy. Flipping a paddy could produce a pound of worms for a hungry bear.

Dave tells me that Yellowstone's worms are probably not native to the area because native earthworms are mostly absent in regions that were glaciated during the ice age. High elevation areas like Yellowstone were likely re-colonized by worms from the family *Lumbricidae,* which came from Europe. Worms are found in association with non-native bluegrass and could be related to the introduction of exotic plants into the GYE. In turn, the worms created soil conditions favoring bluegrass.

Ants

It seems ironic that the mightiest carnivores of the GYE find one of the ecosystem's smallest creatures to be nutritionally important, but they do. Bears will go out of their way to feed on ants. During July and August, ants may comprise 35 percent of the volume of scat, and a single scat may contain 500 to 2,000 ants.

In the GYE, grizzlies use 24 different ant species for food, although only eight commonly. We can group these ants into four

Sometimes bears eat ants by digging up ant nests, like the one shown here. While the reward per ant is small, eating large numbers of ants may supply significant nutrition at critical times during the year.

categories: mound, log, rock, and field. Different species of mound ants (primarily genus *Formica*) build either thatch or rock mounds. Log ants found under logs (*Formica* sp) are a different species than those found inside logs (primarily *Camponotus modoc/herculeanus*). Carpenter ants (*Camponotus*) are the biggest ants.

Bears selectively feed on ants. Large ants are favored, which means that more carpenter ants are eaten than other species, and more ants are eaten later in the season after they are grown. Carpenter ants may have more fat than other ant species, but carpenter ants are aggressive and fast, making them difficult targets. Smaller ants under logs and rocks are consumed less often. However, ants under logs and rocks are consumed earlier in the season; perhaps sunlight warms their nests, causing them to be more active and develop more rapidly.

Bears will rip open ant mounds, tear into infested logs, and dig deep into the ground to expose the inner galleries and chambers of ant nests. As ants swarm out a bear may lick them off the ground or lay beside the mound, raking ants into its mouth. Bears may wait as ants swarm over their paws and then lick them off, reducing the amount of soil ingested.

Sometimes the effort expended for an ant meal seems excessive, but Dave Mattson points out ants may provide significant nutrition, especially at critical times of the year. Carpenter ants provide about 0.03 calories per ant while other ants provide about 0.007 calories per ant. However, the great number of ants that can be eaten quickly makes up for the small reward per ant.

Crude protein may be as important as calories. A bear needs as much as 35 percent crude protein in its diet to maintain energy metabolism. Ants average about 40 percent crude protein. In early summer ants contribute to the building of muscle, and ant eating peaks in August when the meat supply from elk, bison, and fish is at its lowest point of the summer.

How do bears select a particular log to tear open for ants? Can bears hear the ants or smell them? Or is it just luck? Bears walking down a trail will often leave horizontal claw marks across tree trunks. Could this be a way of testing the wood for ants? Does the bear listen or feel for a response that means ants are present? Bears dig holes into the trunks of standing dead trees, creating tunnels towards the centers of the trees where I find ant galleries. Tunnels speed the decay of these trees and soon they fall down, making large numbers of ants more accessible.

Some people suggest that bears eat ants simply as "candy." Their reasoning is that ants are armed with formic acid to ward off foes. Formic acid is tart and may tickle the bear's palette, providing an enticement to eat ants. But research suggests formic acid may impair a bear's digestive efficiency. Does the pleasure outweigh the cost? The ant-candy theory has not been fully explored.

Wasps, hornets, and bees

Wasps, sometimes called hornets (*Vespula*), are social insects. Unlike their less-aggressive relatives the paper wasps (*Polistes*) which have hanging nests, hornets' nests may be in stumps or in the ground. Little is known about these insects in the GYE except that they sting and bears eat them.

Bears also take advantage of bees, delighting in their honey. In the GYE most bee predation occurs on hives maintained by people. Wild hives are few and little is known about GYE bears feeding on wild bees.

According to Dave Mattson, grizzlies in Yellowstone studies consumed few wasps and bees. Remains of these insects were generally less than one percent of total scat volume. The lack of feeding evidence suggests that wasps and bee are not a major source of energy or nutrients. However, wasps and bees may be important

to some bears at some times. As with ants, feeding on wasps and bees peaks in August, a time when animal protein is minimal. When whitebark pine nut crops are low, wasp and bee consumption is higher. During dry years bears seem to feed more on wasps and bees. The highest level of feeding occurred during the extremely dry year of 1988, when the remains of wasps and bees accounted for six percent of scat volume. Perhaps wasps and bees help offset grazing during very dry periods.

One morning my class and I discovered a wasp nest that had been excavated by a black bear. The bear had dug a hole about 18 inches in diameter and 14 inches deep. Our class of perhaps 20 people studied the excavation and the nest remnants for several minutes, creating considerable noise and ground vibrations but no wasps had appeared.

A student asked how long it had been since the bear had been there. I explained that by blowing on the fine dirt around the bear's claw marks we could tell how consolidated the dirt was, thereby gaining a hint of how long it had been since the bear dined. I stuck my head into the hole and blew. Instantly the air was full of defensive wasps. They were pouring out of a hole below the nest. We all ran but the wasps struck several of us on the fly.

The incident reminded us that wasps and bears may have strategies as predator and prey. Since entrances to subterranean nests are hidden, bears may locate nests by smell or by observing wasps entering and leaving the nest. If bears do look for wasp movements to find nests, then swarming out of the nest every time the wasps feel ground vibrations or hear noises might not be a good strategy. It might be better to stay still.

But if a predator has located a nest and is about to dig it up, a swarming response might save it. What if wasps sensed a predator's breath, perhaps its warmth or carbon dioxide, as the predator prepared to dig? Then wasps might swarm in an attempt to drive off the predator. Perhaps that is what happened when I blew into the nest hole. On the other hand, bears might learn that blowing on a nest could make wasps continue an attack, providing food for the bear for a longer time. Perhaps bears feed on wasps in the colder hours of the day when wasps move more slowly.

Grasshoppers, locusts, and Mormon crickets

As I watched, the male grizzly snapped its jaws left and right as it moved across the dry hillside of Mount Washburn. Through my binoculars the reason for his agitation was not apparent. When he left, a close inspection of the area revealed his food source: grasshoppers. Collectively, grasshoppers, locusts, and Mormon crickets are large protein masses moving through open grass meadows. But they move quickly except when it is cold. Mattson suggests that most feeding on these insects occurs on cool days or during early mornings.

Moths

One source of grizzly nutrition went largely unappreciated by bear lovers until the late 1980s when biologists tracking radio-collared bears kept seeing the bears going to alpine rockslides high in the mountains. Soon the reason was discovered: moths.

The moth's scientific name is *Euxoa auxiliaries*. Its common name is army cutworm moth. Every year thousands of army cutworm moths migrate up to 300 miles to alpine tundra in the GYE, arriving around the end of June at the onset of the flowering season. At twilight they feed on wildflowers, converting plant nectar to body fat. During the day they rest under rocks, usually in large boulder fields.

Each moth is a nutrient prize. When they arrive in early summer, their bodies are about 30 percent fats. By late August they are 72 percent fat, 28 percent protein, and only 1 percent carbohydrate. The energy provided by a moth is about 7.9 kilocalories per gram, a level higher than blueberries (4.5), trout (5.7), and even deer and elk (7.3).

Of course, individual moths are small, about the size of a large bumblebee, but among the alpine rocks they gather in concentrations from dozens to thousands. Bears lumber among the rocks like prospectors, turning over boulders large and small. Bears appear to locate the moths by scent, perhaps by moth pheromones.

Dave Mattson and Steve and Marilyn French brought the importance of these areas in Yellowstone to light. During the late 1980s Steve and Marilyn lived in the high mountains studying bears that came to moth aggregation sites. Today we know of more than 50 confirmed and possible feeding sites.

Moth sites vary from two to 40 acres and are located at an average of 10,900 feet in elevation. Rocks tumble into the sites from higher up. Occasionally bears are struck by rocks, and one female black bear was known to have been killed by a rock. About 95 percent of the moth-eating bears are grizzlies. When grizzlies are present, black bears usually feed on the edges of the sites.

In the summer, army cutworm moths migrate to alpine meadows to feast on flower nectar. Although only the size of a bumblebee, each moth is a nutrient prize, and bears eat hundreds if not thousands of moths per day. HILLARY ROBISON

LEARNING TO EAT MOTHS—AGAIN?

Bears feeding on moths were reported in northwest Montana in the 1940s, but historical information in the GYE is rare. Occasionally an old hunting guide will remember seeing grizzlies in alpine rock fields.

Dave Mattson suggests that 1985 through 1987 may represent the critical period for this knowledge in the GYE. For years some radio-collared bears roamed the Absaroka Mountains on Yellowstone's northern border, but there was little indication that the bears ate moths at alpine sites. Bear 106, a radio-collared female, would spend some time above treeline and then go back down. Once she was observed in an alpine area but she was eating biscuit roots. In 1985 the team located her radio signal in "one hell-of-a-spot to get to" and that summer she spent considerable time above treeline.

The next year Bear 106 returned to the same site in July and stayed into September. This time researchers discovered she was eating moths, the first radio-collared bear known to use a moth site. By 1988, seven sites had been documented. The sites were widely separated and each site was used by different bears. Since the bears could not have learned from each other, they must have discovered moths on their own and changed their behavioral patterns to exploit a nutritionally valuable resource.

This widespread, essentially simultaneous change in behavior raises interesting questions. Were the moth sites always there? Had bears lost their knowledge of the sites during the garbage-dump days within the park? It is possible that grizzlies which were redistributing themselves after the dump closures discovered (or rediscovered) moth sites?

Another interesting issue is climate change. Chuck Schwartz, project leader of the IGBST, ponders the effects of a potentially warming climate on moths. If there is significant warming, cold-adapted alpine flora might be lost and trees may be able to grow at higher elevations. Could moths adapt if meadows of alpine wildflowers give way to forests? Chuck notes there is anecdotal evidence that moths may be able to survive in forests, but would they still be accessible in large numbers to bears? Perhaps we shall find out.

A grizzly searches for army cutworm moths in an alpine rockslide.
WILLIAM CAMPBELL

Moth sites are cold, often below freezing late at night. Low temperatures may serve as a defense against parasitic moths that would lay eggs in cutworm moths. However, when bears move rocks to expose moths, the insects are also too cold to fly away. Instead they crawl deeper into the jumble of rocks. Eventually they are blocked from further escape by frozen soil. Bears feed in the cool temperatures of early morning and late evening, resting in day beds at other times.

Several grizzlies often feed at the same moth site at the same time, often in close proximity to each other. The French's once observed 23 bears on one site. Surprisingly, there appeared to be little social tension. Different sexes and age classes mingled. Females with cubs often fed near adult males. Only twice were females observed charging males, and in both cases the males had come between the females and their cubs. In general, adult males were not aggressive to females or cubs and often moved around or away from them. Adult males occasionally chased off other adult males.

Starting in August and continuing through September, moths migrate back to the plains. There the females lay eggs in the soil, and larvae hatch and feed on plants until it is time to hibernate. In early spring, the larvae emerge as cutworms to feed on leafy plants, including crops such as wheat, barley, oats, and alfalfa. The worms then pupate underground, emerging as winged adults in late spring and early summer. They fly to the mountains to feed and mate.

The French's emphasized the importance of moth sites by finding that each site contained one to three female grizzlies with cubs, including cubs of the year. Additionally, many moths remain available into hyperphagia when sources of fatty foods are critical to bears.

Given the importance of moths as grizzly food, biologists will have to focus attention on the agricultural phases of this winged fat

supply. Hillary Robison, a graduate student, analyzed moths at GYE sites for agricultural pesticides. She did find pesticides but in amounts so low they were unlikely to be toxic to bears. The low levels were expected since moths accumulate most of their body fat in alpine areas where pesticides are not used. My own research shows that moths may carry substantial loads of plant fertilizer to the alpine areas.

Although current agricultural use of pesticides to control moths does not appear to pose a threat to bears, agricultural practices change and bears have unique physiology, including hyperphagia and hibernation. Due vigilance should be exercised by ursophiles. As far-fetched as it may sound, effective methods of controlling moths on farmlands might negatively impact bears in the mountains hundreds of miles away.

Cutthroat trout

Because of their spawning habits, Yellowstone cutthroat trout are a key food source for grizzlies. In the spring, cutthroat trout from Yellowstone Lake migrate up small tributary streams to spawn. In these shallow streams a grizzly catches trout by pinning a fish to the stream bottom or bank with its paws, then grabbing it with its teeth. Cutthroats are 95 percent digestible and are composed of 70 percent protein and 18 percent fat. Additionally, the female trout may be laden with eggs. Such a nutritious food resource cannot be passed up.

Cutthroat spawning may begin the first week of May but it peaks in the middle of June. Some spawning lasts until the middle of August. On average, trout are available in a stream for about 33 days. Most fishing by grizzlies takes place in about 60 of the lake's 124 tributary streams. Unfortunately, fewer bears are using this rich food source, and the reason is alarming: fewer cutthroat trout.

Around most of the lake, fisheries biologists have documented a dramatic decrease in the number of spawning cutthroat trout. Two noteworthy examples are Clear Creek, which has gone from an annual spawning population of about 70,000 trout to only 3,000, and Pelican Creek, where a large spawning population has completely disappeared. Within the lake entire age classes of cutthroat trout are now missing, and large fish from 13 to 17 inches have shown a severe decline. The decline in bear usage of spawning streams corresponds with and is probably a direct result of the decrease in cutthroat numbers and size.

The historic role of cutthroat trout in the diet of Yellowstone grizzlies reflects changes in cutthroat abundance and bear adaptability. In the years after World War II, the lake's cutthroat population was depleted by overfishing, the removal of fish for stocking other waters, and by taking eggs for fish hatcheries. Egg-taking and stocking removals ceased in the mid-1950s, and trout sizes and populations started to increase. By the late 1960s the Craigheads reported grizzlies near trout streams but did not report predation on cutthroat trout. Additional changes to fishing regulations resulted in more large fish just as the garbage dumps closed and bears returned to natural diets. Dan Reinhart, bear biologist, and Mattson suggest that bears fishing for trout increased from the 1970s to the 1980s, a sign of flexible adaptation to changing food resources.

Once a mainstay of food for grizzlies and more than 50 other species, the cutthroat trout population in Yellowstone Lake has declined dramatically. The decline is causing biological reverberations throughout the ecosystem.

Cutthroat trout (*Oncorhynchus clarki*) are the only native trout in the GYE, and Yellowstone National Park is the "premier surviving inland cutthroat fishery in North America." It is estimated that at least 42 species benefit from cutthroat trout. Unfortunately, this important part of Yellowstone's ecology is crashing. The culprits include lake trout, whirling disease, mud snails, drought, and possibly pollutants.

When explorers first reached the GYE, 40 percent of its waters were without fish. In 1881, park managers began stocking non-native species into Yellowstone's pristine streams and lakes. These efforts included the stocking of lake trout (*Salvelinus namaycush*) into Lewis and Heart lakes in the 1890s.

In 1994 lake trout were discovered in Yellowstone Lake. Officials suspect the fish were introduced illegally in the lake. The non-native lake trout impact cutthroat trout in two ways. Large lake trout eat cutthroat trout, consuming about 41 cutthroats per lake trout per year, and younger, smaller lake trout compete with cutthroat trout for the same food.

Unlike cutthroat trout, lake trout don't benefit very many predators. Cutthroat trout spawn in shallow tributary streams where they vulnerable to predation; lake trout spawn in deep lake water. Lake trout also tend to remain deeper in the water year-round than cutthroats, which frequently swim and spawn near the surface and in shallow areas where they may become food for ospreys and other predators.

The National Park Service now operates a gillnetting operation in Yellowstone Lake to remove lake trout. In addition, recreational anglers are required to kill any lake trout they catch. Since 1994 park staff and anglers have removed more than 136,000 lake trout. Some evidence suggests cutthroat trout may be responding to this effort, and control measures will continue indefinitely.

In 1998 whirling disease was discovered in Yellowstone Lake cutthroat trout. Whirling disease probably was introduced to North America about 1956 in a shipment of frozen fish from Europe; since then it has spread over much of the continent. North American species such as cutthroat trout did not evolve with this parasite, so they are particularly vulnerable. Whirling disease is the key factor in the demise of the Pelican Creek trout population and is contributing to the severe decline in the overall fishery.

Whirling disease is caused by a protozoan-like parasite known as *Myxobolus cerebralis*. It travels in the fish's nerves where the fish's immune system does not harm it. The parasite digests the cartilage of young fish, causing deformity, frenzied whirling swimming, and death.

During its life cycle *Myxobolus* passes through two hosts, a trout and a worm (*Tubifex tubifex*). Infected trout die and release spores into the water where they may live for years. Spores infect worms that live in fine sediments such as at the mouth of Pelican Creek. These host worms may actually benefit from warm sediments created by the park's hydrogeothermal activity. The warmer the water, the more Myxobolus cells are excreted by the worms, infecting more trout.

Another exotic species, the New Zealand mudsnail (*Potamopyrgus antipodarum*), has invaded aquatic systems in the GYE. In the park the snail has been found in the Firehole, Gardiner, Gibbon, Madison, and Yellowstone rivers and in Polecat and Nez Perce creeks. Biologists report that the snails favor waters influenced by geothermal features and can reach densities as high as 750,000 snails per square meter.

Mudsnails out-compete native microorganisms and consume most of the stream's primary production. Without this food, native stoneflies, mayflies, and caddisflies decrease. These insects are important foods for trout and birds. Trout may ingest mudsnails, but in their hard shells they pass through the fish's gut without being digested, which means they are of no nutritional value to trout.

Mudsnails reproduce rapidly without mating and have as many as six generations of 50 young per year. Counting reproduction by children and grandchildren, one snail may lead to 300 million new snails in a year.

Mudsnails are spread by birds, mammals, and humans, especially on fishing equipment such as waders and boats. To prevent further spread, anglers and others must clean all gear that has been in infected water before going to new waters.

Since the late 1980s drought conditions have affected cutthroat trout by reducing water levels in tributary streams and in Yellowstone Lake. After hatching in spawning streams, young cutthroat trout swim downstream to the lake, but in low water they become trapped in the spawning streams. Low stream flows also lead to warmer water temperatures, which are less conducive to trout survival and growth.

Another possible threat is volatile organic compounds emitted by snowmobile engines. These compounds (such as benzene and toluene) are currently found in low levels in park streams and continued monitoring is needed to detect any cumulative effect on aquatic organisms and potential bioconcentration of these chemicals in fish and bears.

In the fall of 2005, the U.S. Fish and Wildlife Service began conducting a review to determine if Yellowstone cutthroat trout need protection under the Endangered Species Act. In addition to the threats mentioned above, environmental groups and scientists pointed out the fish has been eliminated from 90 percent of its historic habitat, and its gene pool is shrinking from hybridization with other trout, primarily non-native rainbow trout. Nonetheless, the effort to list the fish as endangered or threatened was denied.

Chris Frissell, a fisheries scientist, still advocates federal intervention. "Given the new and large-scale and probably irreversible threats to the core population (in Yellowstone), it is difficult to believe the population is stable and healthy," he said.

Black bears feed on spawning cutthroat trout when they can. Larger, more aggressive grizzly bears often drive black bears from the best fishing spots.

Because of the importance of cutthroat trout, biologists undertook decades of study to ascertain which bears gained what benefits from the trout. Laura Felicetti analyzed mercury levels in bears to investigate the role of trout consumption. Mercury occurs naturally in Yellowstone Lake. It is ingested by plankton, and in a process called bioaccumulation or bioconcentration it accumulates in trout feeding on plankton. Bears eating fish further concentrate mercury in their body tissues. Since most food eaten by bears contains little mercury—less than six parts per billion (ppb)—eating trout that contain 400 to 600 ppb creates chemical signatures in fish-eating bears.

Bear were sampled by barbed-wire hair snags placed around Yellowstone Lake. If a bear rubbed against the wire while retrieving smelly bait, it left a hair sample. DNA fingerprinting identified the individual bear and told its gender. Since hair accumulates mercury, scientists could estimate how much trout a bear had eaten.

Levels of mercury in grizzlies ranged from 17 to 2,600 ppb. Mercury in male grizzlies averaged four times higher than females, proving that male grizzlies ate more trout than females. On average, males ate 55 trout per year while females ate only eight trout.

Using DNA fingerprinting, Mark Haroldson and IGBST biologists identified 74 different bears that ate trout over a four-year period. Of these, 64 percent were males and 36 percent females. Extrapolating this data to all streams around the lake, Mark estimated that about 68 bears fed on trout each year, or about 14 to 21 percent of the estimated GYE population. Overall, male grizzlies ate about 2,400 trout and females ate 200 trout for a total of 2,600 trout per year. This estimate is considerably less than a previous estimate by researchers Stapp and Hayward of about 21,000 trout eaten annually by grizzlies.

Fewer trout likely results in declining consumption, but bear behavior may also come into play. With fewer fish available, large males may be protecting their fishing areas by driving away females and subordinate males, resulting in fewer bears eating trout. Reinhart and Mattson had previously reported poor reproductive performance in trout-eating female grizzlies. The finding suggests that females may become nutritionally stressed because they are expending time and energy avoiding males instead of fishing.

Cutthroats are under attack on several fronts: drought, lake trout, whirling disease, mud snails, and snowmobile emissions runoff (*See sidebar page 80*). Despite a long history of dynamic usage of cutthroat trout, it may be time for grizzly and black bears to once again adapt to a changing food supply, if they can. Continuation of the cutthroat trout's critical role in Yellowstone may be dependent on what humans do in the near future to protect and recover cutthroat trout in Yellowstone Lake.

Small mammals

While it makes sense for a large carnivore to expend energy obtaining a large mammal such as a moose or elk, the value of an animal as small as a vole is not immediately apparent. After all, an individual vole only weighs about an ounce.

Often called field mice, voles (*Microtus*) have short tails and relatively small eyes and ears. They have multiple litters from April to October and produce many young per year. Voles eat the leaves of grasses and forbs, and they cache roots of forbs for winter food. One vole cache contained almost all onion grass, which is 5 percent protein, 8 percent starch, and 57 percent digestible. Importantly, voles increase food caching as winter approaches.

Mattson discovered vole remains in only one percent of grizzly scat, which seems to indicate that voles are a minor part of a grizzly's diet. Vole remains were common in April and grizzlies often excavated vole root caches from gentle, south-facing slopes in September. Bears may

These serpentine mounds of dirt are actually made in the winter by pocket gophers, a grizzly bear food source. In the winter as gophers dig underground, they remove the excavated dirt by packing it into long tunnels in the snowpack. Some snow tunnels may be several feet off the ground. As snow melts in the spring, the dirt casts come to rest on the ground.

Pocket gophers (*Thomomys talpoides*) have been described as furry earthworms because they remain underground 95 percent of the time, digging tunnels. Nonetheless, gophers typically reveal their presence by soil deposited on top of the ground. During the summer when gophers tunnel through the ground to find food, they open a tunnel and shove excavated soil to the surface as a mound. To protect themselves from predators, they plug the mound's entrance hole with dirt.

In the winter when snow covers the ground, gophers make tunnels through the snow. They take the excavated snow into their earthen tunnels where the snow melts and the water seeps away. Gophers then push soil from their underground tunnels into the empty snow tunnels. If the snow pack is deep, the snow tunnels might be several feet above the ground. Each spring the dirt casts of snow tunnels are gently laid on the ground as the snow pack gradually melts. The resulting long sections of tunnel casts on top of the ground makes it appear as though the tunnels were made at the ground/snow interface, but in reality most tunnels were constructed higher in the snow.

Pocket gophers are about the same size and weight as a quarter-pound stick of butter. Unlike chipmunks that carry food inside their cheeks, pocket gophers have external cheek pouches. Gophers can insert roots into their pouches with their mouths closed. The pouches are fur-lined, providing a smooth surface to slide roots. Equally unusual, lips of the gopher seal behind the incisors so that the gopher does not get dirt in its mouth when digging.

Gophers dig tunnels to expose roots of plants such as biscuitroot, onion grass, springbeauty, and yampah. While they eat some roots as they dig, they store most roots in underground caches that they use when food is hard to find or digging is impaired by frozen soil. A root cache may be larger than a basketball.

benefit more from eating voles, either young or adults in the nests, than from raiding vole food caches. However, during dry years and in late fall when other protein is scarce, both voles and their caches may provide important nutrients. Vole caches are smaller than those of pocket gophers, but are similar in food quality and require less digging.

Gophers and their root caches are important food sources for GYE grizzlies. Digging for gophers and their nests and root caches may occupy 20 to 25 percent of a grizzly's foraging in the spring. Grizzlies usually dig for gophers on relatively flat areas where snow pack provided insulation for gophers during the winter. Successful grizzly exploitation of caches correlated with the wettest months, April and May, and with high densities of springbeauty. After snow cover disappeared in June, exploitation of caches dropped dramatically. Successful exploitation of nests at hairgrass and wheatgrass sites took place later in the summer.

Pocket gophers evolved in the southwestern United States and Mexico during the last ice age about two million years ago. Prior to 1850 the distribution of grizzly bears overlapped with the distribution of pocket gophers, but today, because of the diminished range of grizzly bears, the gopher/grizzly relationship persists in only one location, the Greater Yellowstone Ecosystem. It is, as Mattson suggests, a unique predator/prey relationship that was almost lost.

In Alaska and Canada grizzlies feed enthusiastically on ground squirrels, often expending inordinate amounts of energy digging a squirrel out of its burrow. South of Canada, however, grizzly exploitation of ground squirrels is minimal. Only in the GYE are grizzlies known to dig for underground rodents with any frequency, and the rodent of choice is the pocket gopher. GYE grizzlies only rarely dig for ground squirrels.

Large mammals

Deer, elk, moose, sheep, and bison are known as ungulates, a term referring to their multi-chambered stomachs. Ungulates are large food sources for grizzlies. On average, elk calves weigh 40 pounds at birth, 300 pounds as yearlings, 500 pounds as adult females, and 600 pounds as adult males. For moose, the average weights are: fall calves 400 pounds, adult females 850 pounds, and adult males 1000 pounds. For bison, the average weights are: calves at birth 50 pounds, yearlings 350 pounds, adult females 1,000 pounds, and adult males 1,700 pounds.

Ungulates are a major source of protein and fat. The proportion of protein to fat in ungulates changes during the year. In the spring elk are 80 percent protein and 18 percent fat. By fall, elk are 45 percent protein and 53 percent fat. For moose and bison the proportions change from 81 percent protein and 15 percent fat in the spring to 53 percent protein and 43 percent fat in the fall. These changing ratios make ungulates ideal food sources for bears. In the spring ungulate meat provides protein that is necessary to develop a bear's body muscles. In the fall they furnish fat that the bears need to enter hibernation.

The blood-stained face on this grizzly bear indicates that it just fed on an animal carcass. Meat is especially important for grizzly bears in years of poor whitebark pine cone production.

Eating ungulate meat is highly efficient for bears. Ungulates are from 90 to 96 percent digestible. That is, for every 100 pounds of ungulate that the bear eats, it can convert about 95 pounds to its own fat and protein. Moreover, ungulates provide 4.5 calories per gram, far more than such food as berries (2.8), whitebark pine nuts (2.5), roots (2.5) and especially fall grass (0.7).

Of course, obtaining ungulate meat is often far more difficult than obtaining plants, but the nutritional rewards are so great that bears have developed several strategies for hunting and scavenging. These strategies are described in the next section.

During hyperphagia a carcass may become the focus of a bear's feeding frenzy. Rather than leave a valuable food source, this female black bear fed, drank, lounged, and slept near an elk carcass for days.

Each year a chronological dance of seasonal events takes place across the stage of the GYE. The study of the timing of seasonal events is known as phenology and includes both the unfolding of climate forces and biological responses. A bear's menu is dependent on seasonal events.

Bears are temporal opportunists. In general, worms, gopher caches, and carcasses in the spring give way to greening grass and fish in early summer, which give way to ants and mice and voles, which give way to pine nuts. The temporal opportunist is also a temporal omnivore, taking advantage of plant or animal food.

Millennia of feast and famine and starvation and potbellies have taught bears when and where food may be found. Bears must know where to go each day to obtain food. Bears must know where to go next if a food crop fails. Bears must be flexible to compensate for changing foods.

Knowledge of foods is passed down from mother to offspring. The loss of a mother may mean her cubs do not learn how and when to feed. Hungry cubs may starve or get into trouble looking for food.

The loss of a single food source may be compensated with another item, but what happens when two food sources are lost? Three? Four? When cutthroat trout, army cutworm moths, and whitebark pine nuts are all lost? When elk and bison populations drop? When a changing climate changes the vegetation? What is the limit of the grizzly's flexible compensation?

I cannot give the reader the answers but concern lies heavy on my mind. I do know we must preserve all food items whenever possible.

A lush meadow makes for a lazy summer day as a male black bear lounges and feeds on vegetation.

2. POPULATION BIOLOGY
Numbers

On most any night in any bar in the GYE you can start an argument about how many grizzly bears live in the ecosystem. Everyone will be convinced they are correct, their information is the best, and they have a friend who really, *really* knows. Generally the friend also knows what the government is hiding. (Did you ever try to hide a grizzly bear?)

Barroom debate or not, knowing the number of grizzlies in the GYE is critical to solving management dilemmas about the future of the bears. Truth is, knowing the number is no trivial task. Chuck Schwartz and the Interagency Grizzly Bear Study Team estimate that grizzlies occupy about 13,300 square miles in the GYE. If the current bear population is between 400 and 600 bears, that is only one bear for every 22 to 33 square miles. The GYE is some of the most rugged and remote country in the lower 48 states. Imagine finding one bear in 30 square miles, let alone finding every bear.

The task of counting grizzlies has hampered scientists and managers since Yellowstone National Park was established. It is a problem of dollars, people power, and commitment versus distance, ruggedness, and difficult-to-see bears. Each generation of scientists and managers has added to the efficiency with which bear numbers are estimated but it is not possible to count every grizzly.

In 1975 Richard Knight took over the IGBST and was given the task of estimating the grizzly population. The goal was to determine a counting method that was relatively easy to do and one that even untrained personnel could help do. Everyone can recognize a grizzly bear cub-of-the-year. They are small, they don't look like adult bears, they're always with their mothers, and they're so cute they get everyone's attention. So the strategy was that all agencies would collect sightings of females with COY and turn them in to Knight. Every fall for about 20 years, Dick took the reports and, following certain rules, created the minimum estimated number of female grizzlies with COY.

Then a simple equation was used to estimate the total number of grizzlies in the GYE. The equation was based on basic grizzly biology: on average, 1) females stay with young two years, 2) females mate in the second year, giving birth to another litter in the third year, and 3) based on earlier studies, 27.4 percent of females have COY each spring. To calculate the total number of grizzlies, add up the minimum number of females with COY for three years and divide by 27.4 percent. For example if 40, 41, and 42 females were reported to have COY in a consecutive three-year span, then 123 total females divided by 27.4 percent equals 449 grizzlies in the ecosystem for that three year period.

No one has ever claimed the estimating system was perfect, and over the years many scientists have helped tweak the numbers and assumptions. Using the best methods and comparing methods, the best current estimate is 500 to 600 grizzlies in the GYE.

Population trends

Other characteristics of bear biology help managers understand the "health" and status of bear populations. One of the most important factors is whether a population is increasing, decreasing, or stable, i.e. the trend of its "health." Trend can be called vigor or growth rate. Mathematically, if the difference in population from one year to the next is positive, the population grew; if the difference is zero the population was stable; and if the number is negative, the population decreased. Biologically, vigor is determined by the number of births versus the number of deaths (reproduction versus mortality).

Several factors influence reproduction and the number of births, including age at first reproduction, litter size, and time between litters. The more that researchers know about reproductive performance, then the better understanding managers will have about how the grizzly population is faring. Chuck Schwartz and members of the IGBST have recently completed a series of studies pulling together knowledge gathered between 1983 and 2002. Their data on reproduction follow.

The average age when female grizzlies first gave birth was 5.8 years. The average litter size was two cubs. Approximately 18 percent of females had one cub, 61 percent had two, and 22 percent had three. While no COY litters were observed with four cubs, a female was observed with four yearlings. On average, 31 percent of females were observed with COY each year and the interval between litters was 3.2 years. Importantly, the average number of cubs per litter was directly related to whitebark pine production, suggesting that good years for cone production facilitated larger litters.

Other findings suggested that, on average, grizzly bear reproduction peaks between eight and nine years of age and then litter sizes become smaller. Female reproduction drops rapidly beginning at 28 years of age. The expected reproductive span of a female grizzly is about 24 years.

Information on survivorship and mortality is also critical to understand trends. Chuck's team recognized three geographic zones of grizzly populations in the GYE: inside Yellowstone National Park (YNP), outside the park but inside the recognized and protected Recovery Zone (ZONE), and outside the Recovery Zone (OUT). The Recovery Zone is an area surrounding the park where the various land management agencies have agreed to emphasize the protection of grizzly bears. The Zone encompasses about 9,200 square miles. (If grizzly bears are taken off the Endangered Species list, the Zone will be called the Primary Conservation Area.)

Survival of grizzlies was highly dependent on where bears spent most of their time. Survival of cubs and yearlings was highest in the

In recent years, the GYE grizzly population has grown as the number of females giving birth has risen. This is a mother grizzly with two-year-old cubs. Soon the cubs will be on their own.

ZONE, less in YNP, but lowest in OUT. Sub-adults and adults had the lowest survivorship in OUT.

Survival of cubs and yearlings decreased with increasing density of bears. However, higher survival rates correlated with increased whitebark pine nut production, increased winter severity (creating more winter-killed ungulate carcasses for bears to feed on in the spring), and large litter sizes. Survival for adults also increased with higher whitebark pine nut production. For older grizzlies, females survived better than males, averaging about 95 percent survival between years.

Importantly, between 1983 and 2002 survival increased in YNP and in ZONE but decreased in OUT. This variance suggests what Chuck calls a source-sink model. Since more bears are produced within secure source areas (YNP and ZONE), some bears from these areas (especially dispersing young adults) move to areas of lower bear density in OUT. Unfortunately, the probability of death is higher in OUT (due mainly to conflicts with humans), and the OUT population declines each year with more deaths than births. This steady state of decline is sustained only because of the regular influx of bears from YNP and ZONE.

When all years and all areas were considered, the overall trend from 1982 to 2002 was positive. The grizzly population increased.

Distribution

Where grizzlies roam can be thought of two ways: by regions and by habitats. In 1804 when Lewis and Clark documented grizzly bears, the bears roamed across most of the western states and the Great Plains. By 1900 the bears had been eliminated from 98 percent of their historic range south of the Canadian border. By 1922 only 37 isolated populations were known and by 1975 only six remained. The loss of distribution in the Lower 48 states was devastating and played an important role in listing grizzly bears under the Endangered Species Act.

Regional

Since 1973, from hand-drawn maps to modern Geographic Information Systems (GIS), researchers including Basile, Blanchard, Knight, and Mattson have mapped the distribution of grizzlies in the GYE. Chuck and his team developed three types of new maps for 1990 to 2000. They were based on the areas occupied by females with COY (8,800 square miles), locations of radio-collared bears

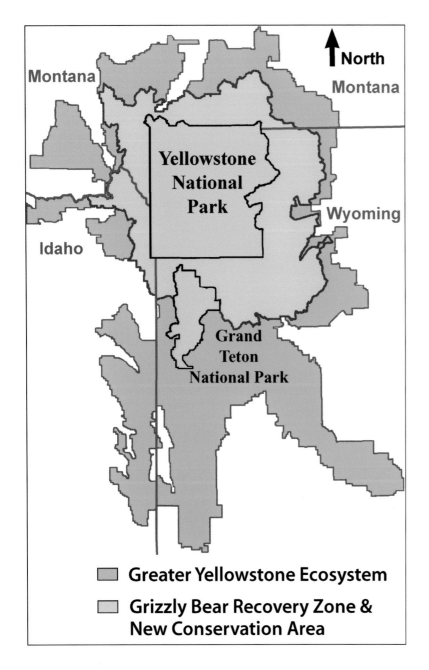

North

Montana

Montana

Yellowstone
National
Park

Wyoming

Idaho

Grand
Teton
National Park

■ **Greater Yellowstone Ecosystem**

■ **Grizzly Bear Recovery Zone &
New Conservation Area**

(10,300 square miles), and conflict situations between bears and people (11,800 square miles). Locations of conflicts with people and resultant grizzly deaths are often the first indications of bears being outside of their expected ranges.

Depending on the map, 17 to 35 percent of the area occupied by grizzly bears was outside the Recovery Zone. Combining the three maps showed that grizzlies occupied 13,300 square miles during the 1990s.

Based solely on females with COY, occupied grizzly range expanded by 48 percent from 1970s to the 1990s. If all three maps are considered, then expansion has been even greater.

Sanjay Pyare and his colleagues studied the dynamics of changes in the grizzly bear range in the southern portion of the GYE. Using historical records, they created maps of the GYE grizzly bear range for every 20-year period since 1900.

A period of range retraction started prior to 1900. By the 1920s grizzlies held on only in the high, remote mountains of the Wind Rivers, Teton Range, Salt River Range, Wyoming Ranges, and Yellowstone National Park. By 1940 they were found only in YNP and just south into Wyoming's Absaroka Mountains. Starting in the 1940s, grizzly range expanded south across the GYE. By 1960 grizzlies were found on the east side of Grand Teton National Park (GTNP). During the 1960s bears began to occupy northeast GTNP. By 2000 grizzlies had reoccupied nearly half of their former GYE range and moved to the northern Wind Rivers and Shoshone National Forest.

The map shows key aspects of the GYE grizzly bear range, including source zones within Yellowstone National Park, the Recovery Zone (to be called the Primary Conservation Area after delisting), and exterior sink zones where protection is limited.

Sanjay explained that the 20th century included a period of range retraction for most large carnivores and since then few have reoccupied their former ranges. Sanjay argued that knowledge of "spatial collapse and subsequent expansion can help frame future conservation efforts." Re-occupancy occurred at an exponential rate, suggesting total occupancy of southern GYE could occur within another 20 years. If a more conservative approach is taken, total occupancy of the southern GYE could occur in 100 years.

Range expansion accelerated when bears were protected under the Endangered Species Act. This period provides a framework and timeline for evaluating future needs and conflicts. Future range expansion will depend on public acceptance of grizzly bears outside the Recovery Zone. It will also be hindered by habitat fragmentation and increasing human populations. Sanjay explains that "an assessment of the difference between biological possibility and the reality of expansion is necessary to focus attention on future carnivore conservation efforts." With this heads up, it may be possible to preemptively mitigate conflicts and predict upcoming needs.

Habitat

For an individual grizzly the location of its relatives across North America is not important. What is important is the area that bear can roam. Is the habitat good or bad? Are there linkages from one habitat to another? Do humans prevent the use of a habitat? How large must a bear's range be to include enough habitats to survive? And in the long-term, how secure is that habitat from human development and from ecological changes such as fires and insect invasions?

The array of habitats known and used by bears is impressive, and bears are very selective in their choices. To understand habitat selection and to determine the value of different habitats, Mattson and colleagues analyzed habitats and their productivity by assessing nutritional value for bears. Based on bear behavioral activities (digging roots, grazing and browsing, cone hunting, insect and mammal predation), they recognized 18 key habitat types (10 forested and eight non-forested). Habitat types are dependent on elevation and available moisture. Forest habitats included plant communities dominated by spruce, Douglas-fir, lodgepole, or whitebark pine, and openings in forests made by fires or timber harvest. Non-forest habitats included talus slopes, rock ridges, meadows and grasslands, marshes and wetlands. Each habitat provides different food sources

Grizzly bear survival is dependent on the continued availability of natural habitat. Human encroachment on bear habitat is one of the greatest threats to Yellowstone grizzlies.

of different nutritional value at different times of the year. That value determines when and where a bear will visit a habitat and explains a bear's seasonal patterns.

Here is a description of the general pattern: After emergence from dens, bears move down in elevation to snow-free areas to look for food. They stay in low-elevation, snow-free areas seeking carcasses, especially bison, and greening grass. In late spring some bears move to cutthroat trout fisheries and by summer other bears are at moth aggregation sites. As plants at lower elevations dry out during the summer, bears move up the mountains looking for vegetation that is still green and nutritious, which may be found in

Protecting grizzlies (like the one above) means securing critical habitat where the bears may roam. On a seasonal basis Yellowstone National Park closes Bear Management Areas (RIGHT) to insure there are places where bears may live, mate, and forage without human interference.

deep ravines and avalanche chutes that retain snow late into the summer. In the fall when even high elevations are dry, bears move down the mountains again. Even bears that had moved to whitebark pine areas will move to lower elevations if nut production is poor. These general patterns can vary each year, depending on snowmelt and summer moisture.

Home ranges and movements

The hallmark of the grizzly's remarkable ability to survive under human onslaught is its ability to be in the right place at the right time to sustain its nutritional needs. This means a bear must have a large home range with many different sources of food and know where those foods are. Additionally, the grizzly must be able to adapt to the failure of a food source and find other food that is available. Of course, searching for alternative food sources when natural foods fail is the main reason grizzlies get into conflicts with people.

YNP has set aside selected areas within the park to provide seclusion for grizzlies. Called Bear Management Areas (BMA), these backcountry sites are closed at certain times each year to everyone (except for rare trips by administrative or research personnel) so

bears may live, mate, and forage without being bothered by humans. BMAs enclose key habitats and are sources of grizzly survival.

Since bears continually explore, the longer a bear lives the larger its lifetime home range becomes. The lifetime home range contains all components necessary for survival. A bear's specific location within its home range depends on the food available at that time.

Measuring the size of a home range is tricky because of annual and seasonal complexities. Bonnie Blanchard and Dick Knight provided some of the best estimates of annual home ranges for Yellowstone grizzlies. Adult males averaged about 875 square miles while subadult males averaged about 700 square miles.

Home ranges of adult females depended on the presence and age of cubs. When alone or with COY, the annual home range was about 230 square miles, but when a female was with yearlings, the range averaged about 400 square miles. It is interesting to speculate that perhaps the small size of the range when a female is with COY relates to the inability of the short-legged cubs to travel far, whereas with yearlings it is necessary to teach them the geography of their future home ranges so they travel greater distances. The average dispersal by cubs from maternal home range is less than 20 miles.

The larger sizes of male home ranges may result from males needing more food because they grow larger, or from having to travel to find mates. Females show more fidelity to a smaller home range that is adequate for nutritional needs. A smaller range that is well known by a female may also provide additional security.

The range of a male may overlap with that of several females. However, males tend to avoid each other and large adult males tend to have little overlap. The core ranges of the males seldom overlap. (Core range is the geographical area most often used by a bear.) Seasonal ranges may be connected by travel corridors into an annual home range.

Grizzlies typically don't travel far from day to day, probably averaging about a mile for males. However, some travel may be abrupt and direct, such as going to a winter den. The Craigheads reported one grizzly traveling 32 miles in 62 hours.

Sources, sinks, and links

Given that grizzlies do travel to find suitable habitat, is there enough habitat in the GYE for bears to survive and is there any additional habitat not currently in use? Troy Merrill and Dave Mattson explored these questions through the use of mathematical and GIS models. The resulting look at the GYE revealed two types of suitable habitat, core and transition. All other habitat was classified as unsuitable.

Habitat quality was defined as habitat productivity (from Dave's research mentioned previously) versus human activity (the more human activity, e.g. road density, the less likely bears were to survive). Productivity versus activity represented births minus deaths and good habitat required positive values indicating positive population growth.

One model found that potential core grizzly habitat covered more than 10,600 square miles and represented the most remote and productive places in the GYE. Four regions of core habitat were larger than 347 square miles, the average life range of a female grizzly. The main core habitat was centered on Yellowstone National Park. The other three core areas were the Centennial, Palisades, and Wind River areas, separated by 12, 28, and 18 miles from the Yellowstone core. Core areas were surrounded and connected by suitable transition habitat of lesser but acceptable quality.

Next, Troy and Dave developed a landscape mortality risk model which mapped "source" and "sink" areas for grizzly populations. Areas where birth rates would exceed death rates were source areas. Sink areas were the opposite. This model was based on past locations of grizzly deaths along with landscape features correlated to bear deaths or bear survival, such as grazing allotments, wilderness areas, and national parks. Potential source habitat was defined as areas where annual probability of human-caused death was less than six percent and habitat productivity would be enough for bears to feed, survive, and reproduce. Sink habitat was defined as having a probability of human-caused death greater than six percent annually.

The landscape-mortality risk model classified 18,700 square miles as source areas and 31,000 square miles as sink areas. (Obviously there are a lot of areas where a grizzly can get in trouble!) This model defined the areas where the average grizzly bear could survive long enough to replace itself. Source areas were larger than core areas and included all cores areas.

The two models suggest that not only is there enough habitat for GYE grizzlies to survive, but additional areas outside of the current distribution of bears would support grizzly populations. If bears were moved to outlying source areas, the GYE might support as many as 115 additional bears in separated populations.

Separated populations offer potential protections and problems. On the positive side, a localized catastrophe such as a disease might not affect other populations. On the other hand, small, isolated populations are more vulnerable to food shortages, genetic inbreeding, and other problems, and they are, in general, less likely to survive than larger populations. Since two of the potential source areas are separated from the central Yellowstone region by sinks, they might require periodic translocation of bears to supplement the genetic makeup of those populations.

Translocations can be avoided if linkage zones can be established between core areas of the GYE, and even along all of the Rocky Mountains. The designation "Y 2 Y" is both a movement and an organization designed to link core habitat areas. Originally named for Yellowstone to Yukon, it has also been dubbed Yukon to Yucatan. The premise is to preserve and protect remaining wild areas so wildlife may move freely along natural corridors.

Steve Primm and Seth Wilson point out that "discussions of reconnecting grizzly bear populations has often been preoccupied with ecological information needs and technical solutionsÒrather than the sociocultural dimensions of conservation." Steve and Seth suggest that small-scale projects involving local people can demonstrate success and build political support for linkage habitat conservation. Linkage is the wave of the future and one of our best hopes, not only for bears but also for all wildlife and habitat in the west.

A subadult male grizzly gazes at its human observers. Bears need bear-favorable habitat connected by linkage routes where they can travel safely. It is up to humans to provide these safe havens.

3. PREDATION AND SCAVENGING

Predation

If an animal is big and fast and has big canine teeth, then predation comes naturally to that animal. Yellowstone's bears fit this description and they are consummate predators when opportunities arise. They also have strategies to maximize success.

Standing along the Mount Washburn road, we used spotting scopes to scan the south side of Specimen Ridge. We watched a grizzly running for no apparent reason. The bear went back and forth over the hillside for more than a half mile. It went up and down a thousand vertical feet. It loped, not at a top speed but faster than any distance runner could match. It weaved in and around three-foot-tall sagebrush. This activity went on for about 30 minutes. Then an elk calf flushed from sagebrush near the bear. A surge of speed by the grizzly and the hunt was over. The bear's seemingly endless jaunt was actually a well-developed strategy that produced food.

Kerry Gunther, Yellowstone National Park's bear management biologist, and Steve and Marilyn French describe three hunting strategies when bears are preying on elk calves: search, chase, and ambush.

Searching takes advantage of an elk's strategy to protect calves by having calves curl up on the ground in an area of tall sagebrush and remain motionless. Grizzlies search in one of two ways. During blind searches, a bear approaches a sagebrush meadow where there are no elk. It moves rapidly through the sage with its nose to the ground.

Generally the bear uses a zigzag pattern and sometimes stands on its hind legs to look for newborns. These searches average about 30 minutes but they may cover two miles and last two hours before the bear is successful or gives up.

The visible search involves a bear charging into a meadow where there are elk, usually females. But rather than chase the fleeing adults, the bear starts searching through the sage just like a blind search.

Many people say newborn elk calves have no odor. This is not true. After performing a necropsy on a dead calf, I can smell the calf's odor on my hands, and if I can smell it, so can a bear. Many observers have seen searching bears abruptly turn into the wind and grab a calf. Nonetheless, when a calf curls among the sagebrush its odor is low to the ground and doesn't dissipate very far. A bear must be close to detect it.

In a chase, a bear lopes towards a herd of elk, causing them to bunch together. Then the bear charges into the herd, scattering the elk and creating confusion. Sometimes calves get separated from their mothers and the bear concentrates on a calf. Chases average only five to ten minutes but may cover three miles.

FACING PAGE: *Carefully watched by a herd of cow elk, a grizzly wanders through Antelope Creek Valley. The bear is grazing on grass but constantly alert for a hidden elk calf.*

RIGHT: *Grizzlies lie in wait or sneak through brush to ambush elk. Bursting from their hiding places at full gallop, successful grizzlies usually catch their prey within 20 seconds and in less than 150 yards.*

The third strategy is ambush. This is when bears take advantage of cover, usually trees, to stalk as close as 50 yards from elk. Then the bear bursts from hiding at full gallop. Ambush chases are very efficient and seldom last more than 20 seconds or cover more than 150 yards.

To a certain extent, the type of hunting strategy is dependent on the development of elk calves. Most calves are born in the last week of May and the first weeks of June. When first born, the calf cannot run well so to hide it lays still, its spotted pelage helping to provide concealment. At this time a bear needs to smell the calf, flush it out of hiding, or stumble upon it. As the calf gets older and stronger, it travels with the herd but a fast or skillful grizzly can separate a calf from the herd and chase it down. Bears try to get the herd running in circles. Then the bear exerts a burst of speed and cuts across the inside of the circle to take down a calf. As a calf continues to develop coordination and speed, it can outrun a bear in a straightaway chase. Then the bear's best strategy is to get very close and ambush it.

Take down is usually accomplished by the bear grabbing the elk on the rump with its paws and using its weight to collapse the animal, or by swatting the hindquarters with its paws and knocking the elk off its feet. Bears do not swat at the head. Sometimes calves simply stumble and bears quickly pounce on them.

Bears occasionally catch small calves on the run by snatching them in their mouths. Bears quickly stand on the prey and use a bite to kill it. Bears often pick up calves in their mouths and shake them vigorously. Often the bear will pick up a calf and carry it into the woods to feed. Occasionally, if the grizzly is suddenly distracted, I have seen captured calves get up and run off.

Lone bears and females with cubs do much of the predation on elk calves. The time when calves are most vulnerable coincides with the bear mating season, and adult males spend far more time searching for females than preying on elk calves.

Elk often act in defense during bear attacks on calves. A mother elk will approach a bear that is searching her area. If the bear chases the mother, the adult elk is seldom caught and the bear usually ends up starting a new search in a new area, presumably away from where the mother elk had hidden her calf.

In a chase, mother elk sometimes charge at the bear from the side, causing the bear to veer off and perhaps lose track of calf it was chasing. At other times not only the calf's mother but other female

LEFT: *The food prize for this adult male grizzly is a road-killed bison. Most of the meat is already gone but it is still a treasure of nourishment.*

FACING PAGE: *Bears, especially grizzlies, are possessive of their food. After feeding, a bear often buries the carcass with whatever material is nearby, including grass, sticks, and dirt. When hungry, the bear uncovers the carcass and feeds again. Sometimes a bear will even lie on the carcass to defend it from other scavengers.*

elk will cross between a running calf and the pursuing bear. Occasionally a female will try to intimidate a bear and may actually kick at it. The final defense strategy is to flee into water, usually a river. This tactic works better with wolves than grizzlies.

Summer chases of adult elk are more often failures than successes. Much has been made about grizzlies killing large bull elk that are in a weakened condition after the autumn rutting season, but this has seldom been observed. Mattson calculates that on average a Yellowstone grizzly kills an adult elk once every year. Of course, some grizzlies kill no elk and other grizzlies kill more than one. Some of these elk must be bulls.

Some bears must prey on elk after dark. Female bears with cubs may not come out of the forest until dark, but by morning light they are seen feeding on a freshly killed elk carcass.

Bears occasionally kill more animals than they can eat. This behavior is called surplus killing. Reports of killing three calves at a time are not unusual. Steve and Marilyn French once saw a grizzly kill five calves in 15 minutes. That is the highest number I have heard. Surplus-killed animals may be cached or abandoned.

Predation on elk calves provides a significant amount of meat in May and June. Kerry Gunther reported that the success rate for predation on elk calves in Pelican Valley decreased from 70 percent in May to 60 percent by mid-June to 30 percent by the end of June to zero by the end of the first week of July. Elk calf predation is mostly over by mid-July; by then the calves can outrun the bears.

Grizzlies also prey on moose and bison. When Dave Mattson compared prey selection, grizzlies appeared to favor moose over other ungulates while bison and deer were least favored. Bears obtained almost half of their moose meat by predation; on average a bear killed one moose every other year. Nonetheless, the amount of moose meat consumed by grizzlies was 20 times greater than would be expected by the population density of moose.

Moose are larger than elk and usually provide more meat, but moose behavior may be the critical key to bear predation. Moose are

solitary creatures that inhabit forests much of the time. Grizzlies may be better able to use forest cover to stalk and ambush moose. Conversely, elk and bison exist in herds in open areas, two factors that work against successful bear attacks.

Few deer are taken, possibly because deer are fast and in general inhabit lower elevations than grizzlies.

Because of its large size, a bison represents a valuable food prize for a bear, but with size comes the ability to defend itself. Bison are very agile and have been known to run 40 mph for great distances. They are very strong with powerful head and shoulder muscles. Given the risks of injury to a bear, it was not surprising there were almost no historic records of bears preying on bison. In 2002 that changed.

On June 26, 2002, Yellowstone naturalist Nathan Varley along with Bob Landis and Joel Sartore, National Geographic videographer and photographer respectively, watched a female grizzly with two COY approach a lone bison and her calf. The calf appeared to be seven to eight weeks old.

The grizzly stared intently at the bison and her calf. The bear and her cubs ambled into some sagebrush where the bear suddenly picked up speed and headed down the slope to intersect the walking bison. The bison sped up but the bear cut them off.

Initially the mother bison was between her calf and the bear. When the bison turned to confront the grizzly, the bear went around her. The animals disappeared in a swale, and then the bear came out of the swale with the bison calf in its mouth and the mother bison in swift pursuit. The bear stopped to defend its catch. The mother bison

circled and sort of bluff charged, but she was not really trying to gore or trample the bear. Finally the bison started to eat grass about 20 yards away; this was obviously displacement behavior at not being able to get the grizzly to leave.

The bear fed on the calf for 15 minutes and the mother bison left. Then the bear covered the carcass with grass and sage. She found her cubs and together they disappeared into the woods. At dusk the entire family came to the carcass and fed.

Rare as this attack was, another bear attack on bison was recorded on September 23, 2002, this time by Travis Wyman, park bear biologist. It happened at Fishing Bridge. A female grizzly with two COY approached a young adult bull bison. The bear charged and the bison ran. The bear swatted the bison's hind feet from beneath it and the bull slid down an embankment with the bear riding on top of it. They slid into a tree and finally stopped on a boardwalk.

A battle ensued but the bison was at a disadvantage, having broken its left front leg. The bear inflected considerable injuries but couldn't make the kill. Five times the bear left the bison and then came back. Finally, at dark and five hours after the start of the attack, she went into the trees.

Whether obtained by predation or scavenging, meat is an important part of a grizzly bear's diet in the GYE. Nonetheless, bears are omnivorous, eating plants and meat. A grizzly's long claws are more often used to dig plants than to capture prey.

Due to the danger the situation posed to people, the bison was dispatched by park personnel and the carcass was moved away from the road. The next day the female returned with her cubs and fed on the carcass. Travis believes the bear would have eventually killed the bison but the natural end was thwarted because of the presence of people.

While some female grizzlies are very adept at predation, most predation probably is done by males. The reasons may be two-fold. A risk of injury is always associated with predation, especially on large animals such as moose and bison. For a female bear, an injury might signal the end of her ability to care for her young.

Another reason, according to Dave Mattson, is that different life strategies for males and females may influence the need for active predation. Reproductive success of a female is dependent on sufficient reserves of adipose fat, whereas males need muscle to gain competitive advantage in a breeding system often characterized by violent confrontations with other males and even with females. Since a high-protein diet promotes muscle growth, greater consumption of protein by males would be expected.

Predation by bears significantly impacts ungulate herds each year. The late Francis Singer, park biologist, estimated that during the late 1980s grizzlies killed about 950 elk calves on the northern range in the park each summer, and that grizzly predation equaled the number of elk calves taken by coyotes and black bears combined. Since wolf reintroduction, Doug Smith of the Yellowstone Wolf Project believes grizzlies take about 50 percent of the calves killed each summer and wolves take only about 10 percent. Mattson estimates that before wolves arrived grizzlies used predation to procure 30 percent of the ungulate meat that they consumed. On average, this equated to an adult grizzly killing 1.4 to 5.8 ungulates per year. In Grand Teton National Park where grizzlies were largely absent, black bears were the major predator on elk calves, accounting for more than 45 percent of known calf mortality.

Efficiency of elk predation may be an acquired skill. From 1935 to 1967, elk in Yellowstone were maintained at an artificially low level of 5000 animals. During this time, bears fed at garbage dumps and feeding arenas. When the elk reduction program terminated and the dumps were closed, bears reverted to natural food. As the number of elk increased, opportunities for predation increased. Since females with young are involved in predation, young bears may learn predation skills from their mothers. The recent increase in the bison population and incidents of predation on bison may represent the beginning of a similar learning process.

Grizzly predation on cattle southeast of the park recently increased. In an area with 17 grizzlies, three adult males were responsible for the majority of predation, killing as many as 16 cows each. The only other four grizzlies known to prey on cattle killed but one animal each. Grizzly predation on cattle is opportunistic. Management removal of habitually predatory grizzlies nearly stopped the cattle predation.

Predator-naive ungulate species developed following the extirpation of grizzlies from most of their former range in the GYE, according to Joel Berger, behavioralist for the Wildlife Conservation Society. Joel believes generations of ungulates grew up without significant predation by grizzly bears or wolves. By the time grizzlies started to recolonize and disperse south of Yellowstone, most prey no longer sensed the great bear as a predator. Joel tested the naivetÈ of Grand Teton moose by exposing them to urine and feces of grizzlies, black bears, wolves, and coyotes, and to recorded calls of wolves. He compared his results to Alaskan areas where carnivores were major factors.

In Grand Teton, predator-naive animals were less sensitive to auditory and olfactory cues. In Yellowstone and Alaska where moose co-existed with bears and wolves, such cues elicited increased vigilance. Moose from predator zones were also more aggressive when confronted with odors. Increased predation on moose south of Yellowstone suggests that naive moose are more susceptible to the new predator in their area, the grizzly bear.

If predation on naive species were swift and highly effective, then the potential exists for a species to be extirpated. To survive, prey species need to rapidly develop recognition and avoidance skills. Joel found that cow moose in Jackson Hole that lost their young to newly arrived wolves elevated their vigilance to recorded wolf calls by about 500 percent. Loss of offspring may make mothers hypersensitive to predator cues and facilitate development of defense mechanisms.

Scavenging

Scavenging is safer than predation, and with their great ability to smell, bears are very adept at locating carcasses. Mattson estimates that 57 percent of elk, 54 percent of moose, and 96 percent of bison

meat consumed by bears comes from scavenging. Most of the scavenged meat is adult male bison, elk less than 24 months of age, and adult female elk. Interestingly, scavenging provides grizzlies with essentially the same amount of meat as they obtain by predation.

Soon after den emergence, bears locate winterkilled ungulates to eat whatever meat remains on the carcasses. Summer provides few opportunities for predation or scavenging.

Fall brings the rut, or mating season, for elk and moose and a renewed opportunity for both predation and scavenging. Elk rut in September, moose in September and October. Male elk and moose become more vulnerable to predation by being disoriented with sexual interests, weakened by extended mating efforts, or injured or

When grizzly bears (LEFT) and black bears (RIGHT) bears emerge from hibernation, scavenging on winter-killed elk or bison is vital to survival. Bears search large areas and often locate thawing carcasses by smell. The winter-softened meat seems delectable to bears.

killed in fights with other males. Fatally wounded ungulates provide considerable meat for scavenging bears.

The role of scavenging varies from year to year and is dependent on factors such as weather and plant production. Ungulate use by bears is inversely related to whitebark pine crops. In good whitebark years, bears consume less meat. During and after exceptionally harsh winters, the number of winterkilled carcasses may reach saturation levels; not every carcass may be visited by a major scavenger or all the meat eaten at a scavenged carcass.

Predation and scavenging together provide the greatest annual energy input for grizzly nutrition. Mattson estimates that ungulate meat contributes 70 percent of total energy needs for males and 56 percent for females (not considering energy needs for reproduction and lactation). The contributions can be broken up as follows: 53 percent from elk, 24 percent from bison, 18 percent from moose, 4 percent from livestock, and 1 percent from deer.

Prior to wolf reintroduction, the average adult grizzly consumed, by predation and scavenging, 5.5 to 13.8 ungulates per year to meet these energy levels. Today, wolves successfully prey on elk all year, providing bears with increased access to carcasses. The restored dynamic between wolves and bears is described later in this section.

On average, grizzlies are able to obtain more food from an animal when they kill it than when they scavenge it (because other scavengers may have already taken meat from the carcass before the bear found it). However, the size of the food source makes a difference. Grizzlies kill more elk but obtain as much meat from bison by scavenging.

For a grizzly, developing the ability to locate a carcass is a critical skill. Especially in the spring when meat is important for bears to recoup from hibernation, a bear's ability to cover great distances and use its powerful sense of smell provides important rewards.

Competition

Bears must compete with other bears and other species for available prey and carrion. Competitors include other large carnivores and a host of small carnivores and scavengers. Competition may be within a species (grizzlies versus grizzlies) or between species, such as grizzlies versus wolves. Predation itself may be related to competition. For example, if a grizzly kills and eats a black bear then the black bear cannot compete with the grizzly for mutually desirable whitebark pine nuts.

Competition may be either direct or indirect. Direct or encounter competition might involve a fight between two grizzlies at a fishing stream or a fight between a grizzly and a mountain lion over a carcass. Indirect or interference competition occurs when one animal reduces the amount of a resource, such as food or mates, available to another animal. For example, if a raven scavenges meat from a carcass being fed on by a grizzly, the grizzly has lost food to interference competition.

At first glance, competition from ravens may seem insignificant but it adds up. A single raven may consume two pounds of food from a carcass per day. Multiply one raven by fifty ravens, a number not unusual on a carcass, and the amount of available meat can be quickly reduced.

Ravens are only one of the competitive scavengers in the GYE. Others include magpies, Clark's nutcrackers, grey jays, crows, bald eagles, golden eagles, turkey vultures, black bears, red foxes, coyotes, wolves, and even wolverines.

Because of competition, edible biomass on a carcass disappears quickly. Jerry Green, bear biologist, discovered that half of an average-sized elk carcass is consumed in the first 24 hours after its death. Bison, being larger, take more time, and smaller-bodied animals disappear faster. If a grizzly does not find a carcass in the first few days after death, most food will be gone.

BEARS AND FIRES

Wildfires usually don't threaten bears. In fact, bears may graze at the edge of the flames, and nutrients released by fires fertilize lush growths of grasses and herbs, enticing bears into recently burned areas.

Yellowstone has provided a natural laboratory into ecological interactions between grizzlies and wildfire. Yellowstone is a fire-based ecosystem where fire provides for the regeneration of forests, especially those dominated by lodgepole pine. Over 30 natural ignitions may occur each year. However, 1988 was anything but average. Heavy fuel accumulation and unprecedented drought conditions allowed nearly 1,000,000 acres to burn.

Bonnie Blanchard and Dick Knight worked their way through fire restrictions to monitor the interaction of 38 radio-collared grizzlies and other bears during and after the fires. Because of flight restrictions, most of their information deals with the bears after the fires had passed.

The bears largely ignored the fires. On most days a bear could stay in front of a fire by walking. Two radio-collared grizzlies disappeared during fires which swept over the valleys they were known to be frequenting, but one was trapped again a year later. Thirteen bears moved into burned areas after the fire front passed, three remained in active burns, and three stayed outside fire lines.

Bears moving into burned areas often walked among smoldering or burning logs. They fed on emerging sedges and grasses, dug for insects in logs and anthills, and excavated roots. Mostly, however, bears fed on ungulate carcasses. Between 100 and 500 ungulates were estimated to have died in the 1988 fires. Scavenging was scattered, but scat analysis showed that bears were consuming more meat than normal. Only small amounts of meat were eaten at each carcass; only about 13 percent of all available meat was consumed. Bears seldom paused to bury a carcass.

After the fires were over, key behavioral changes occurred. The summer of 1988 had presented extremely bad food conditions for bears due to the drought, but after October 1 there was only one management action involving a grizzly compared to an average of six management actions in other autumns of low food availability. Bears were eating the fire carcasses.

The fires of 1988 showed several things. Bears usually can avoid the flames but quickly return to burned areas to take advantage of available food. Extensive fires may provide sufficient food to ameliorate the negative effects of drought and poor whitebark pine crops. Fires appeared to have no effect on denning activities, as den locations did not shift.

Competition for food doesn't always come from other bears and other large carnivores. A single raven may eat or remove about two pounds of meat from a carcass per day, so this flock of ravens could "steal" a significant amount of meat from this grizzly bear.

Encounter competition is rarely observed. As expected by their location at the top of the ecological food web, carnivores are widely distributed and have low population densities. Seldom do two carnivores come together and when they do, most often they exit the scene in opposite directions. But not always.

Dave Mattson has summarized some known predation by grizzlies on grizzlies in Yellowstone. In two incidents COY were killed, in another a yearling female, and in one a young adult male. Two animals had broken vertebrae or puncture wounds to the back, while the third had a crushed skull with canine tooth marks. All the killed bears were small.

The evidence suggests that predation on bears occurs mostly in the spring at locations where several bears may be seeking food. Most grizzly-on-grizzly predation is probably done by adult males, as supported by two known kills by male grizzlies. Predation on small or young bears seems disproportionately high. Incidentally, one of the cubs of female grizzly 264 was found with a broken pelvis and had to be euthanized. There was weak evidence that the cub had been attacked by a male.

Encounter competition comes into play during grizzly-on-grizzly predation. By killing another grizzly, the victorious bear may secure additional food resources or gain a reproductive partner. A female bear that loses her young to predation, including cubs killed by a male grizzly, may experience another estrus cycle and become available for mating. Since male grizzlies roam great distances and encounter many females, the probability of a male killing its own cubs is low, and by gaining another chance to mate, a cub-killing male grizzly may leave more of its genes behind, which is the goal of genetic competition.

Encounter competition between species doesn't have to result in direct physical harm but can simply result in the loss of food for one of the species. This outcome is seen in competition between bears and cougars. Our detailed knowledge of these rare events was uncovered by Kerry Murphy, park wildlife biologist, and his team of researchers. Kerry and his colleagues actually tracked cougars on the ground for continuous periods of time. They were able to find kills made by cougars and search for signs of bears that either fed on the cougar kills or displaced cougars from the kills.

On average, bears visited one in three kills made by cougars. The highest level of visitation (42 percent) occurred in the spring. At about one of every eight kills, bears displaced cougars, forcing the cats to eat later or to abandon their kills. Bears consumed about four pounds of meat per day from cougar kills, and by moving cougars off their kills before they were finished eating, bears deprived cougars of a pound and a half of meat per day.

These quantities of meat are significant in the energy budgets of each animal. Four pounds of ungulate meat is about the equivalent of 2,800 calories, a significant amount of energy for any bear. The loss of a pound and a half of meat for the cougar amounts to a loss of about 25 percent of its daily needs.

Coyotes can provide significant and fatal encounters with bears. One day at Slough Creek I videoed a young lone grizzly as it wandered across a hillside. The bear wandered near a coyote's den and three coyotes quickly attacked. Nipping at the rump of the bear, the coyotes soon got the bear moving at full gallop. One coyote charged in and grabbed the grizzly by its right hind foot, causing the bear to roll end-over-end in a cloud of dust. Thoroughly routed by this unexpected turn of events, the grizzly regained its footing and started to gallop off, but before the bear could cover one stride a coyote bit it on the rump, hastening its departure. On other occasions I have seen coyotes hasten or lead grizzlies away from their dens.

Coyotes can be successful predators on bears. Bob Landis filmed six coyotes killing a black bear COY even though its mother tried to defend it. One day near Tower I saw coyotes nearly kill a black bear COY but the cub was able to escape by climbing a tree.

LEFT: *Coyotes also compete with bears. Often a coyote will feed at one end of a carcass while a grizzly feeds at the other end.*

FACING PAGE: *Grizzly bears and wolves once again share the Yellowstone landscape. For bears, the reintroduction of wolves has brought both benefits and dangers. Here a grizzly bear and wolf eye each other over an elk carcass.*
PETE AND ALICE BENGEYFIELD

Bears and wolves

The grizzly's role as Yellowstone's undisputed top predator ended in January 1995 when wolves were reintroduced to Yellowstone. While a single wolf is smaller than a grizzly, packs of wolves outweigh even the largest grizzly and have more animals capable of inflicting wounds. Given each species' need for ungulate meat, wolf reintroduction set the stage for encounters between wolves and grizzlies.

Kerry Gunther and Doug Smith, head of the Yellowstone Wolf project, documented 96 interactions between wolves and bears in Yellowstone National Park. The outcomes of the interactions varied.

At five carcasses involving female grizzlies with cubs, wolves displaced bears three times. Bears displaced wolves one time. The one time the bears "won," a female grizzly with two COY displaced six wolves. During the encounter, wolves temporarily stopped the approaching bears by circling them. The bears were forced to turn and defend themselves. The mother and cubs all lunged at the wolves. Once at the carcass, the bears scavenged with little harassment by wolves. When the bears left, the wolves did not harass them.

Wolf packs establish rendezvous sites where pack members gather and rest. A wandering bear may enter a rendezvous site and when it does, the wolves usually become alert and approach the bear. They will walk with the bear until it leaves the site.

Wolves will attack mother bears with cubs. One snowy day in the Lamar Valley a female grizzly and a COY started towards a carcass and were attacked by two wolves. The wolves circled the mother, biting at her rump. When the bear turned to go after one wolf, the other wolf would try to grab the cub. With her front foot, the female would scoop the cub under her belly to protect it. Having to protect the cub, the mother bear could never take more than a couple of steps towards the wolves. Eventually the wolves left and the bears retreated up a hillside out of the valley.

A few days earlier just as dark descended a female grizzly with two COY had been seen near the den site of the Druid Peak wolf pack in the Lamar Valley. In the morning, observers in the area saw a female grizzly with one COY. Was this the same family group? If so, what happened to the other cub? I believe the wolves killed the other cub that night. With two cubs and perhaps being attacked by more wolves, the female probably could not have successfully protected both cubs.

To date, it appears that wolves have killed at least four grizzly cubs, although the actual killings have not been witnessed. Kerry Gunther and Doug Smith once found the carcass of a 50-pound female cub after observers reported 10 wolves from the Druid Peak pack sniffing, chewing, and playing with the carcass. The body was largely intact; less than five percent of it had been consumed.

When wolves greatly outnumber a bear, the bear usually retreats. One day I witnessed about 20 wolves circling an adult grizzly and harassing it until it left. Another time 35 wolves chased a lone adult grizzly up Jasper Bench and out of their area. Against such numbers an adult grizzly might be killed.

Which species wins a dispute over a carcass may depend on motivation. A hungry female grizzly with cubs may drive off some wolves. But more often, wolves motivated by hunger drive off bears. One spring morning Bob Landis videoed four members of Druid Peak wolf pack approach a grizzly on a carcass south of Soda Butte. It was probably a young adult male bear.

The wolves initially drove off the grizzly with a surprise attack. Then the bear returned, scattered the wolves, and took a position on top of the carcass. For the next 30 minutes a battle ensued over and around the carcass. The wolves' strategy was to bite the unprotected rump of the bear. The bear had to spin constantly to protect its rump. When the bear was drawn from the carcass, it would quickly sit down to protect its rear and look back over its shoulders for attacking wolves.

While one wolf attacked, another wolf would take a bite out of the carcass. Eventually the bear gave up and left. The wolves fed for about 30 minutes until their bellies were distended with meat. Then a second, slightly larger male grizzly arrived. For perhaps 10 minutes the wolves

A pack of wolves could be a threat to this yearling black bear.
Wolves in Yellowstone have been known to kill grizzly cubs.

harassed the new bear but then walked off and went to sleep. Wolves with full stomachs are less motivated than hungry wolves.

Dan MacNulty and Nathan Varley witnessed an exciting encounter between wolves and a grizzly in Pelican Valley. In March 2000 while watching a sequence of continuous interactions between grizzlies and wolves, five wolves attacked an 11-month-old bison calf. As they watched, a grizzly appeared and eventually displaced the two wolves at the rear of the struggling calf. Three wolves still gripped the front of the calf but the bear pulled it away from them. Then the bear killed the calf and ate it.

Direct competition between wolves and bears may impose significant selective pressure on bears. It is not necessary to kill an adult bear to impact the bear population. Predation on cubs alone can doom the population. However, there is an offsetting benefit to the presence of wolves: additional meat for bears.

Two trends have developed. Dan MacNulty and his team have shown that in Pelican Valley grizzlies are increasingly dependent on wolves. When grizzles come out of hibernation, they quickly locate wolves in the valley and follow them to feed on their kills. Doug Smith reported that within one day, every wolf kill had been usurped by a grizzly.

There is a double significance to the Pelican Valley story. Because of deep snows, elk leave the valley in the winter and only bison remain there. However, the success ratio of grizzlies killing bison is next to zero. On the other hand, wolves occasionally do kill bison and then the grizzlies may benefit. Besides, if a wolf is hurt attacking a bison, it is of no consequence to the bear.

In the fall as food becomes scarce, some grizzlies have started "adopting" wolf packs. Bill Hamblin, a bear watcher, saw such an event during the fall of 2002. On October 25 Hamblin and Wayne Kendall spotted the Geode wolf pack near Tower Junction. The pack was being followed by an adult grizzly wearing a red radio-collar.

The next day the wolves killed an elk on Hellroaring Plateau. The bear, identified by the red collar, usurped the kill and ate its fill. For two days the wolves and the grizzly alternately fed on the carcass until the food supply gave out. The wolves left first. About 40 minutes later when the wolves went out of sight, the bear left they carcass. Nose to the ground, it followed the exact route taken by the wolves. On October 31 Hamblin saw the Leopold wolf pack bedded by a local landmark called Frog Rock. At dusk the pack got up to leave and the red-collared bear was with them. As the wolves trailed out of the area, the bear followed.

Bears with full stomachs may not hibernate, and the availability of wolf kills may be affecting hibernation patterns. In Glacier National Park where wolves established themselves in the mid-1980s, biologists have noted grizzly tracks every month of the year. On Alaska's Kodiak Island, male grizzlies that have access to food at low elevations do not hibernate. Lately in Yellowstone, grizzlies or their tracks have been observed as late as December 31 and as early as February 1. It is possible that more available food may allow Yellowstone grizzlies to remain out of hibernation.

Elk hunting by humans

From an ecological standpoint, human hunting of elk outside of the park creates significant potential for scavenging and competition. Elk killed and wounded by hunters generate considerable meat in the ecosystem. A 1986 report calculated that hunters provided about 500 tons of meat from gut piles (the internal organs from field-dressed deer and elk) and discarded animal parts in areas north and south of the park. Elk accounted for 370 tons of the total. For bears and other carnivores, a meat source is a meat source and cannot be disregarded.

Bears have learned that the hunting season creates reliable and predictable sources of food. In Montana, most hunter harvest occurs in the first week of the hunting season. In Wyoming, harvest is drawn out due to staggered opening dates for different areas and species. Mark Haroldson showed that when the hunting season opened in Montana, grizzlies abruptly migrated north out of the park into Montana. Their migration to the south was more gradual but accounted for many bears moving into hunting areas. In fact, after hunting season opens, the odds of a grizzly being outside of the park is two to four times higher than of it being inside the park. In years of poor whitebark pine nuts, the odds of a grizzly being out of the park during hunting season are even higher.

Hunting creates ecocenters or concentrations of food that draw bears. Increased carnivore density, especially around kills, increases the probability of confrontations among species, including humans. Hunter-caused deaths of grizzlies in the GYE increased in the 1990s, perhaps partially in response to increased numbers of bears and to grizzlies expanding their ranges away from Yellowstone.

A critical question is whether grizzlies coming to these ecocenters have now developed a tradition of "gut pile use." Haroldson's study started in 1983, or about one generation of bears after grizzly hunting was stopped in the GYE. Before then, grizzly utilization of gut piles was presumably lower because grizzlies could be legally shot. Of hunter-caused grizzly deaths since 1983, 56 percent have resulted from chance encounters but 44 percent resulted from encounters at carcasses or when bears sought meat in hunting camps.

Mark believes bears learn quickly and that females pass learned behaviors to their offspring. He suggests that ample time has passed since legal hunting ended for a tradition of gut pile use to develop, and that human hunting provides a source for increased mortality of grizzlies. To reduce conflicts between bears and hunters, IGBST suggests several guidelines for hunters. These include directives to remove edible meat after gutting or field dressing the animal,

eliminate meat processing in camp, and quickly transport meat out of the backcountry.

To find out how the hunting season affected bears, cougars, and wolves, Haroldson and cougar biologist Toni Ruth orchestrated two collaborative studies of elk hunting. (A side note I must add: Toni's paper represents a major maturation of carnivore science since the Craigheads started their work in 1959. Not only did Toni include state-of-science information about the big three carnivores, but her team of scientists combined the talents of leading researchers from across several government agencies—all for the good of carnivores.)

Bear, cougar and wolf researchers simultaneously studied their respective species prior to and during the 1999 hunting season. Three grizzlies, the Rose Creek wolf pack, wolf 9F (wandering alone), and a cougar family consisting of a female and two kittens were monitored for changes in their behaviors.

As Montana's hunting season began, Yellowstone grizzlies shifted their activity range north of the park into the hunting area. Wolves did not change their locations. In addition, the presence of hunters evidently did not push wolves or grizzlies that were already outside of the park back into the park.

Cougars shifted into the park for any of several reasons. Elk do move away from hunters and some elk probably moved back into Yellowstone as hunting started. Cougars shifting into the park may have been simply following their prey, especially since cougars tend to kill prey rather than scavenge meat. Also, cougars are subordinate to both grizzlies and wolves and may have moved to areas of lower predator density to avoid competition. Or cougars may have simply moved away from humans as hunters entered the area.

Pieces of twigs and grasses decorate this black bear cub-of-the-year.

MANAGEMENT & EDUCATION

Scat happens! Paradigms shift! Yellowstone has known all the paradigms of bear management: predator control, feeding platforms, roadside feeding, garbage dumps, relocation, conflict killings, aversive conditioning, and today, roadside viewing, often at very close distances. Across the continent bear-related paradigms are changing. Wildlife managers are learning that one shoe does not fit all. With complex creatures such as bears, there are many correct answers, including different answers for different locations. Different management experiments must be tried and the best solutions selected for each area.

Steve Herrero, Tom Smith, and colleagues argue that bears must be "managed for intrinsic and ecosystem values." Bears are functional parts of ecosystems but humans also hold bears in special, intangible reverence. People need bears! According to bear mythologist Jim Garry, the bear is our teacher. According to the Bear Mother myth, the Bear Mother made it possible for naked apes—humans—to live out of Africa. We learned from the Bear Mother. We learned what to eat, how to clothe ourselves, and in short, how to live. Today we still need the Bear Mother. We are still learning and translating bear knowledge into adaptive management to save the bear and the planet.

From Alaska to Yellowstone, people watch and learn from grizzly bears. A recent public opinion survey in Alaska showed that tourists were willing to pay more to view bears than any other Alaskan wildlife. Yellowstone National Park is the premiere non-coastal

Yellowstone National Park is at the forefront of managing interactions between people and bears. People are controlled so bears can utilize natural foods along roads. Such management also produces good opportunities to see and understand bears.

viewing area for bears in North America. In this regard, Herrero and Smith point out that "managers of bear populations intended primarily for viewing need to help foster positive, reasonably safe experiences with bears."

The evolution of bear management in Yellowstone has come a long way in recent years to allow visitors to stand 25 yards from a female grizzly with cubs. Previous bear management "wasn't working," explained Collette Daigle-Berg, a law enforcement ranger. "Hazing the bears away was politically not good. Visitors wanted to know why Yellowstone was driving away the bears that they had come to see." Slowly, policy shifted to manage the people. People are kept on the roads, whether the bears are close or far away. "Policy is still evolving as we learn more and gain experience with bears along the road," Daigle-Berg said. "We now manage people and let bears do their thing."

Yellowstone's program is called Bear Protection through Education (BPE), and it has made Yellowstone a leader in managing bear viewing. Judy Knuth Folts, deputy chief of the division of interpretation, explained that BPE is a cooperative effort among park divisions to protect visitors and bears while allowing the public to view bears at close distances. The program consists of dedicated, knowledgeable, roadside interpreters for safety control and public education at bear sightings. The primary location for BPE is the roadside, but interpreters take their messages to campgrounds, evening programs, and roadside pullout talks where they explain bear-watching etiquette.

Visitors like the field contact with uniformed rangers. Mark Hanna, a roadside bear interpreter, told me about the people he meets, their attitudes, and what he can convey. Mark says "people have an intangible reverence for bears. Bears are special among all creatures. They are easily recognized even by someone who has never seen a bear."

At bear sightings, Mark's first focus is the safety of the people, then vehicles, traffic, and bears. Mark's message is "take time to share with a wild, natural bear." He explains that bears are not always aggressive. They can be content with people nearby.

Bears that tolerate nearby people are habituated to people. According to Herrero, human-habituated bears conserve energy by muting their reactions to people. But they are still wild bears and can react as wild bears if people transgress.

Collette explains that bears along the roads are often subordinate bears that are actually using humans to secure their space from more aggressive bears. The borrow pits along park roads contain about 80,000 acres of usable bear habitat, and usable habitat is a prime commodity.

Kerry Gunther believes bear watching will work if bears never become more than simply habituated to the presence of people. The big problem, of course, is a food-conditioned bear. If someone feeds human food to a bear, that bear will likely get into trouble trying to secure more human food. As a saying goes: "A fed bear is a dead bear." Always, food conditioning is the downfall of bears.

Habituated bears may face other problems, such as being struck by vehicles or being shot outside of the park, but the positive benefits often outweigh the negatives. When a person experiences a bear, when they experience a wild, free-roaming bear, they are likely to favor bears, other wildlife, and wildlife conservation in the future, even in their voting.

Clearly BPE is working. Mark says, "Yellowstone is the forum for a nation. It is the poster child for the environment of the planet. BPE shows that people can live with bears." Since its inception in 2001, BPE interpreters have talked with more than 200,000 people. Judy pointed out, "It is not the quantity that counts but the quality of experience visitors are having with bears."

Mark remembers a gentleman in his early 60s. He approached Mark with a self-conscious smile and introduced himself. He explained that on family vacations to Yellowstone in the 1950s, he and his family fed the bears. He said his father, who never shopped for food, would buy food specifically for their Yellowstone trips and say, "This is for us and this is for Mr. Bear."

In the 1960s the man watched the Craigheads on *National Geographic* television programs and with renewed interest brought his children to Yellowstone to see bears. He said his kids had gone into careers in the outdoors because of their Yellowstone experiences. In the 1980s the man quit coming to Yellowstone because the "bears were all gone. There were no more bears."

Now the man was back with his grandchildren, and they were watching bears. Listening to Mark made him "happy because he now knew everything was okay and the way they ought to be." Mark said it felt like a confession but he understood the power of the bear and what the gentleman meant.

DELISTING AND THE FUTURE

When historians look back in 100 years, I wonder how they will judge the collective wisdom of *ursophiles*—the public, the rancher, the scientist, the resource manager, and everyone else—on the question of delisting the grizzly bear.

The purpose of the Endangered Species Act is to recover the populations of species so they are no longer considered endangered. Successful recovery is the act's ultimate goal. The act expressed the will of Congress to put the full weight of the federal government into elevating species security to a point where states could manage a formerly endangered species and guarantee its existence in perpetuity. When a species reaches its secure level, the U. S. Fish and Wildlife Service is supposed to take it off the endangered species list. In other words, "delist" it.

If delisting of the grizzly bear in the Lower 48 states takes place, the states will take over complete management of grizzly bears outside of the national parks. The states could, among many management options, resume hunting of grizzly bears, probably on a very controlled basis. Another concern of delisting is that protection of grizzly bear habitat might be diminished in decisions about logging, road building, mining, and other human developments.

There are numerous opinions on both sides of the delisting issue. Some argue that the GYE grizzly bear population has, in fact, recovered; therefore the bear should be taken off the list as the law requires. Delisting is proof that grizzly bears in the GYE have been saved.

Others believe strongly that delisting is premature. They argue that even if the bear population is better now than it used to be, bears

Although roads and bears can co-exist, such as in Yellowstone, too often roads take a toll on bears. Limiting the growth of roads in the Greater Yellowstone Ecosystem will be important in maintaining secure areas for bears.

remain imperiled because of threats to their habitats outside of Yellowstone National Park. The bear's future, they argue, is not assured.

Although it pains me to think about it, I feel obligated to list the gamut of perils shadowing the road to bear survival. I have already described the threats wrought by climate change, drought, diseases, parasites, exotic species, and pollution on delicately balanced populations of whitebark pine, trout, moths, ungulates, and other grizzly foods.

Consider, too, the human population explosion that is reaching the beautiful, remote, pristine, and fragile Greater Yellowstone Ecosystem. The desire for houses drives entrepreneurs of private lands at an exponentially increasing pace to subdivide and develop, thereby fragmenting habitat and preventing wildlife access to food. More houses mean straighter and faster roads with an attendant increase in wildlife killed by vehicles. Logging and petroleum exploration further fragment the ecosystem with roads, well pads, and pollution. Those who move to or visit the ecosystem usually do so to enjoy its recreation in various ways. Legal and illegal use of all-terrain vehicles and snowmobiles, combined with the inability of land management agencies to close roads, reduces the amount of quiet and peaceful habitat, even jeopardizing winter denning sites. In the GYE the habitat of the grizzly bear is far more fragmented, far more developed, and far less secure today than it was when the grizzly was listed as endangered in 1975.

Whatever happens with delisting, a period of legal appeals, reviews, and lawsuits likely will follow. As a biologist, I won't guess how long the future of the grizzly may be tied up in court. *Ursophiles*

There are places where bears belong and should be left untouched, like these grizzly bears relaxing on a Yellowstone hillside. The greatest danger to bears and the GYE is the loss of wild habitat.

need to "stay tuned," follow this issue, and weigh in with their opinions.

I asked Chuck Schwartz, leader of the IGBST, what are the most exciting and important issues of the future. Chuck said the issue for the future will be the interface where an expanding grizzly bear population meets humanity. This is the interface of the source/sink model of grizzly populations, the places where grizzlies thrive and the places where they die. It is at this interface where a dispersing bear population will create problems.

The long-term survival of bears depends on acceptance and balance. Both bears and people have to be considered. There are places where bears do not belong, and in these places bears will need to be removed. Managers must have the flexibility to do their jobs, which will build public acceptance and support of bears. Of course, bears must also have protected areas.

Three issues are paramount: does the public have the will, the means, and the commitment to save grizzly bears.

The "will" is clear. Time and again public surveys have shown that people, both locals and those remote from Yellowstone, support saving the grizzly. As often said, what matters is not necessarily seeing a grizzly but simply knowing there are places still wild enough that grizzlies roam there.

The "means" is clear, too. Through the Endangered Species Act and the concern of all who love wild bears, the GYE grizzly bear population is healthier now than it was 30 years ago. The GYE grizzly is one of the most studied animals on the planet; it is certainly the most studied bear. There are more measures in place to protect its future than any other bear species anywhere. A cadre of dedicated and knowledgeable scientists and managers is in place to follow the troughs and peaks of future population trends. We have learned a great deal about bear biology and bear habitat. Although we don't know everything yet, we have a far better understanding of what bears need to survive.

"Commitment" requires money. It is estimated to cost $3.4 million per year for the U.S. Forest Service and the states of Idaho, Montana, and Wyoming to manage a delisted grizzly bear. *That is more than a million dollars more than current funding.* And the costs could grow. Disturbingly, these additional funds have not been secured, they have not been allocated, and no one knows where the money will come from. It is an odd irony that when it comes to the future of grizzly bears, dollars are my final worry.

If you are concerned, get involved. Learn and become knowledgeable. The appendices in this book list organizations and web sites where you can learn more about bears. Join a group (or more than one) involved with bears. To stay abreast of regional happenings, I recommend the Greater Yellowstone Coalition. For donations where your dollars go directly to helping the Yellowstone grizzly, I recommend Defenders of Wildlife, specifically the Bailey

Compensation Fund that pays for preventive conflict resolution and loss of livestock, and the Bear Management Fund of the Yellowstone Park Foundation, which helps fund research and conflict resolution. These recommendations should in no way reduce your commitment to the other fine organizations listed in the appendix.

With delisting and the future comes more debate about bears. Louisa Wilcox of the Natural Resources Defense Council predicted the following: "The debate will pit the various narratives about bears against each other: bears as intrinsically valuable to humans versus the frontier ethic of developing the land, our obligation to restore imperiled species versus putting people first, our fascination with wild animals versus our fear of being attacked or eaten. Each of us will have an opportunity to redefine what the bear means to us, and *to shape how the story ends* (emphasis mine)."

It has been said that wilderness without wildlife is merely scenery. The Greater Yellowstone Ecosystem is wild, and in many ways it is the grizzly bear that makes it truly wild. Bears and wilderness are inextricably linked. Maintaining both into the future will require vigilance, effort, and determination.

Somewhere in a den deep under the Yellowstone snows, probably in late December 1990 or early January 1991, a little grizzly cub was born. She was destined for fame.

Her first years were lived in obscurity until she and her mother separated. I first became aware of her when she approached, perhaps even charged, a couple of hiking parties on the Grizzly Lake Trail.

During the summer of 1995, she was often seen along the road from Mammoth to Norris Geyser Basin and often in the vicinity of Roaring Mountain. This feature became her namesake—the Roaring Mountain grizzly. On September 23, her fame spread. Lance and Belinda Peck, videographer friends of ours, chronicled the events in *BEARS Magazine* (Winter 1996). By the Twin Lakes turnout, "she made a grand and bold appearance," the Pecks wrote. "People came and went from the bear like a trail of ants."

"Humans seem to get brave when they are in a large group," the Pecks noted. Soon there was "a semi-circle (of people) around the bear and she became agitated. Few in the crowd realized that together they had broached her tolerance of them. She turned broadside, became stiff-legged, and began swaying her head." But the Roaring Mountain grizzly retreated into the woods, averting a bad encounter. The Pecks wrote, "About the only conclusion to make is good bear behavior brings out the worst behavior in some of us."

During the first week of October, the Roaring Mountain grizzly was back by Roaring Mountain. Lance and Belinda backtracked her trail in fresh snow, learning her routine. They made plaster casts of her tracks that are stored in my Track Education Center Museum in Gardiner.

The grizzly successfully killed an elk within 50 yards of the road. Crowds gathered, photographers photographed, videographers videoed.

All went well for several days. The grizzly started covering the carcass with grass and eyeing the crowd. She wanted to leave but seemed afraid that the crowd might get her food. Meat is critical during hyperphagia.

One day she marched directly into the middle of the crowd on the road. She faced south, her body swaying. The crowd retreated. She marched north and the crowd faltered back in confusion. Her facial expression said she was the "biggest, baddest beast around." Rangers maneuvered their vehicles between the bear and the crowds and she returned to her food.

Two days later she again came to the road. "Grizzly-wise viewers" moved back immediately while rangers ordered the "hypnotized watchers" to move back. As she approached the road, she found a hastily abandoned pack which she quickly appropriated and took back to the carcass. Getting human food can lead to a grizzly getting permanently removed. Bear managers acted quickly. They ordered people into their cars and drove off the bear with firecracker shells. An intimidating group of rangers went to the carcass and brought back the pack, squashed banana and all.

Confused and enraged at the loss of her prize, the Roaring Mountain grizzly returned. To protect the public the rangers had also moved the carcass but the bear did not understand. Confused, she ran wildly around the meadow. Managers shot at her with firecracker shells and rubber bullets. Eventually she left. Bear managers knew the importance of her food source and left it for her.

On October 14, 1995, the Roaring Mountain grizzly was trapped and tranquilized. She was fitted with a radio-collar around her neck and numbered tags in her ears (number 459 in her left ear and 460 in the right). She weighed 230 pounds. She was the 264th grizzly radio-collared by the IGBST.

So began the saga of 264 and the public's love affair with this wild grizzly. Over the next few years 264 became a regular roadside attraction and it was not long before she was entertaining thousands of visitors each year. I believe it is accurate to say she became the most photographed grizzly bear in the world.

To the delight of her growing fan club, 264 emerged from hibernation in the spring of 1997 with her first litter, two cubs. The trio of ursids held onlookers transfixed during the summer as she let visitors observe her family at close range along the road.

However, luck was not with 264 and her family. In the fall one cub was crawling behind her sister and mother. Park biologists picked up the cub to see if it could be helped. They took it to the Mammoth Clinic where an X-ray showed that the cub's lower spine was broken. It was euthanized. In all likelihood the cub had been attacked by a male grizzly in the area. Later in the fall the remaining sibling disappeared without a trace.

In 1998 264 again graced the roadside with her presence, and in the spring of 1999 she appeared with two cubs. Both cubs disappeared in May. Her radio-collar ceased to work that year.

In the spring of 2000, 264 again emerged with two cubs. These cubs remained with her until the summer of 2002. In June 2002 264 probably shed her collar.

In 2003 264 showed up without any cubs, much to the disappointment of all who were waiting for her and hoping for a new set of little cubs.

Near Norris Geyser Basin on the night of June 14, 2003, 264 was hit by a car and seriously injured. The driver and witnesses said 264 darted from the timber in front of the car. The driver, going at legal speed, braked and swerved but was unable to miss her. 264's multiple injuries included a broken back. She was euthanized at 4:45 a.m. on June 15. She weighed 258.9 lbs.

The bear world was shocked and saddened. Her fan club held a wake at the Mammoth Visitor Center. The welcome sign at the Super 8 Motel in Gardiner, Montana, was changed to read, "Rest in Peace Bear 264. You will be missed." It is a comfort to know that 264 is survived by two offspring that roam somewhere in the Yellowstone area.

One of 264's fans was Dr. Charles Schwartz, leader of the Interagency Grizzly Bear Study Team. Chuck first saw 264 in 1997 and carefully followed her long career, sharing time with her on several occasions.

Chuck says 264 served as a remarkable visual example of grizzly behavior for the public. Over the years 264 had multiple litters and lost some offspring, both of which are not uncommon for grizzlies. She was a meat eater yet loved to graze on vegetation. She did all this in front of and to the delight of her public. Even her death was a lesson. "Ultimately 264's fate was sealed by the hand of man," Chuck said. "Again she is the example, for the final fate of all bears is with humans."

Leading her two-year-old cubs across a snow patch is grizzly 264. Grizzly 264 was probably seen by more people than any other wild grizzly bear in the world. In many ways she was an example of how the fate of all bears lies with people.

NOTES & RECOMMENDATIONS

1. BEAR SAFETY

It is particularly important to obtain detailed information about how to hike and camp safely in bear country before you engage in these activities. In the space of this book I cannot provide an adequate discussion of these topics. Therefore, I recommend the following sources for this necessary information:

Agencies & organizations

Yellowstone National Park / National Park Service
P.O. Box 168, Yellowstone National Park, WY 82190
Phone 307-344-7381 www.nps.gov/yell

Yellowstone Association
P.O. Box 117, Yellowstone National Park, WY 82190
Phone 307-344-2293 www.YellowstoneAssociation.org
The Yellowstone Association is the park's interpretive association & an excellent source for books, maps, and educational opportunities.

Grand Teton National Park
National Park Service, PO Drawer 170, Moose, WY 83012-0170
Phone 303-339-3300 www.nps.gov/grte

Grand Teton Natural History Association
PO Box 170, Moose, WY 83012
Phone 307-739-3606 www.grandtetonpark.org
GTNHA is Grand Teton's interpretive association and an excellent source for books, maps, and educational opportunities.

Center for Wildlife Information
PO Box 8289, Missoula, MT 59807
www.bebearaware.org
The center has excellent brochures about bear country safety that can be printed from its website.

Bear safety publications

Bear Attacks: Their Causes and Avoidance by Steve Herrero (Globe Pequot, 2002 revised) This book has long been recognized as the most authoritative reference.

Hiking With Grizzlies: Lessons Learned by Tim Rubbert (Riverbend Publishing, 2006) A good book for gaining knowledge and confidence about what to do in a variety of bear encounters. Actual trail encounters in Glacier and Yellowstone national parks were analyzed for the proper responses by hikers. Includes descriptions of two backcountry encounters when the author had to use bear spray on grizzly bears.

Backcountry Bear Basics: A Definitive Guide to Avoiding Unpleasant Encounters by Dave Smith (The Mountaineers, 1997)

Bear Aware by Bill Schneider (Globe Pequot, 1996)

Safe Travel in Bear Country by Gary Brown (Globe Pequot, 1996)

Safety in Bear Country: Video (Magic Lantern Communications, Ltd., Toronto, Ontario, Canada, 800-667-1500). Available from various sites on the Internet.

Living in Bear Country: Guidelines for bear-proofing your property. (Defenders of Wildlife, 2000) A booklet available through Defenders of Wildlife, Northern Rockies Regional Office, 114 W Pine, Missoula, MT 59802 or on their web site.

Bear safety Internet sites

Bear Country: www.fs.fed.us/r1/wildlife/igbc/Safety/cwi/menu.htm

Bear Identification Program: fwp.state.mt.us/bearid/default.htm

Bear Smart: wlapwww.gov.bc.ca/wld/bearsmart/bearsmintro.html

Center for Wildlife Information: www.bebearaware.org

2. BEAR ORGANIZATIONS & EDUCATIONAL OPPORTUNITIES

Bears classes & programs in Yellowstone

A Naturalist's World www.tracknature.com

Teton Science School www.tetonscienceschool.org

Yellowstone Association Institute
www.YellowstoneAssociation.org

Internet news site about Yellowstone's bears

Ralph Maughan's Wildlife Reports www.forwolves.org/ralph

Key government pages about bears

Interagency Grizzly Bear Study Team
www.nrmsc.usgs.gov/research/igbst-home.htm

Interagency Grizzly Bear Committee www.fs.fed.us/r1/wildlife/igbc

Montana Fish, Wildlife, and Parks www.fwp.state.mt.us

Yellowstone National Park
www.nps.gov/yell/animals/bear/index.html

Conservation organizations with specific interest in Yellowstone's bears

Yellowstone Park Foundation www.ypf.org

Defenders of Wildlife www.defenders.org

Greater Yellowstone Coalition www.greateryellowstone.org

National Wildlife Foundation www.nwf.org

Natural Resources Defense Council www.nrdcactionfund.org

Sierra Club www.sierraclub.org/grizzly

Vital Ground www.vitalground.org

Yellowstone to Yukon www.Y2Y.net

National education and research organizations

Craighead Environmental Research Institute
www.grizzlybear.org

Great Bear Foundation www.greatbear.org

International Association for Bear Research and Management
www.bearbiology.com

National Parks Conservation Association
www.npca.org/wildlife_protection/

3. RECOMMENDED READING

Animal Life of Yellowstone National Park by Vernon Bailey (Charles C. Thomas, 1930)

Bears in the Yellowstone by M.P. Skinner (A.C. McClurg and Co., 1925)

Bears - Majestic Creatures of the Wild by Ian Stirling (Rodale Press, 1993)

Bears of the World by Lance Craighead (Voyageur Press, 2000)

Hunting the Grisly and Other Sketches by Theodore Roosevelt (G.P. Putnam's Sons, 1893)

Review of the Grizzly and Big Brown Bears of North America by C. Hart Merriam (North American Fauna No 41., Government Printing Office, 1918)

Population Characteristics and Activities of Black Bears in Yellowstone National Park by Victor G. Barnes, Jr. and Olin E. Bray (Colorado State Univ., 1967)

The Bears of Yellowstone by Paul Schullery (High Plains Publishing Co., Inc., 1992)

The Biography of a Grizzly by Ernest Thompson Seton (The Century Co., 1899)

The Documentary Record of Wolves and Related Wildlife Species in the Yellowstone National Park Area Prior to 1882 by Paul Schulery and Lee Whittlesey (National Park Service, 1992)

The Grizzly Bear by Thomas McNamee (Alfred A. Knopf, Inc., 1982)

The Grizzly Bear - Portraits from Life by Bessie Doak Haynes and Edgar Haynes (University of Oklahoma Press, 1966)

The Grizzly Bears of Yellowstone - Their Ecology in the Yellowstone Ecosystem, 1959-1992 by John J. Craighead, Jay S. Sumner, and John A. Mitchell (Island Press, 1995)

Track of the Grizzly by Frank C. Craighead (Sierra Books, 1979)

Wild Animals At Home by Ernest Thompson Seton (Grosset & Dunlap Publishers, 1913)

Winter, An Ecological Handbook by James C. Halfpenny and Roy Douglas Ozanne (Johnson Publishing Company, 1989)

Yellowstone Grizzly Bear Investigations - Annual Report of the Interagency Grizzly Bear Study Team by the Interagency Grizzly Bear Committee members, annual (Interagency Grizzly Bear Study Team)

Yellowstone National Park Bear Information Book by Kerry Gunther and Mark Biel (Yellowstone Center for Resources, 1995)

Grizzlies in the Mist by Chuck Neal (Homestead Publishing, 2003)

Lives of Grizzlies: Yellowstone and Glacier by Jim Cole (Farcountry, 2004)

MY FINAL GROWL

Science describes the bear, management resolves its conflicts, yet the magic of the bear remains. Is it unprofessional or unscientific to fear for the future of the bear? Is it wrong to worry about bears in this time of climate change and planet turmoil? No! Bears invoke sentiment. As I said in the introduction, "Time will tell how the bears will fare, and all ursophiles need to remain vigilant on their behalf."

Just as it would be wrong for scientists to believe their research was done, or for managers to feel confident that their tasks were accomplished, it would be wrong not to feel sentiment. Science and management cannot distance themselves from the magic of the bear.

It would also be wrong for scientists, managers, and ursophiles not to learn from the past. We—the scientists, the managers, the ursophiles, and the readers of this book—must comprehend the magic of the bear. Let the history in these words of a song by my friend Ron Cisar remind us that we are at the crossroads for bears, for humans, and for planet Earth.

ESCUDILLA By Ron Cisar

Dedicated to the memory of Aldo Leopold

In the southwest there looms a piece of the earth
A mountain that guards o'er the plains
She rises to the heavens and for all that she's worth
Escudilla is her name

She's home to such creatures as squirrels and Jays
The whitetail seeks shelter in her pines
But not long ago a man's bullet passed her way
Changing the course of all time

Chorus:
For on Escudilla there once lived a grizzly
The last of its kind that inhabited there
And each time you'd catch a glimpse of that mountain
You couldn't help but think of the great, grizzly bear

She's bounded by mesas, canyons and woods
Her junipers fragrant the night
And I'd love to see her if only I could
As she catches the dawn's early light

Now mountains with grizzlies are true wilderness
They stand for all that's wild and that's free
But each year a kill would leave a ranch one cow less
The bear was only acting naturally

(Chorus)
The ranchers had stalked him up into the hills
But Ol' Bigfoot knew well his domain
So a government trapper was summoned for the kill
How insensitive, selfish and insane

His efforts were futile, his traps did not lure
This magnificent beast from his lair
But a setgun tripline was placed on Ol' Bigfoot's trail
And a bullet shot out through the air

(Chorus)
Escudilla still looms on the open horizon
Her land is now safe for man's scared cow
But when you gaze at her beauty you don't think of bear....
"It's only a mountain now"

(Chorus)
For on Escudilla there once lived a grizzly
The last of its kind that inhabited there
And each time you'd catch a glimpse of that mountain
You couldn't help but think of the great, grizzly bear
The great grizzly bear ... "It's only a mountain now"
Great grizzly bear ... "It's only a mountain now"
Great grizzly bear ... "It's only a mountain now"

ABOUT THE AUTHOR

Dr. James Halfpenny, a scientist and educator, owns A Naturalist's World, a company dedicated to providing educational programs, books, slide shows, and videos about ecologically important subjects. He is the author of the highly acclaimed *Yellowstone Wolves in the Wild*, a book about the way wolves are living in and changing the ecology of Yellowstone National Park. He is also the author of *A Field Guide to Mammal Tracking in North America*, *Discovering Yellowstone Wolves: Watcher's Guide*, *Tracking: Mastering the Basics* (video), *Winter: an Ecological Handbook*, *Snow Tracking*, *Scats and Tracks of the Rocky Mountains* and other titles in this series, and numerous scientific and popular articles. Since 1961 Jim has taught outdoor education and environmental programs for state, federal, and private organizations, including numerous programs in Yellowstone National Park. Jim may be contacted at:

A Naturalist's World
www.tracknature.com
(406) 848-9458
P.O. Box 989, 206 5th ST W
Gardiner, MT 59030

ABOUT THE PHOTOGRAPHER

Michael H. Francis, trained as a biologist, is a renowned wildlife photographer. His photography has been recognized internationally for its beautiful and informative imagery. He has thirty-four, single-photographer books to his credit, including his latest for Riverbend Publishing, Yellowstone Memories: 30 Years of Photographs & Stories. He maintains a stock file of more than 500,000 images. Mike's work has been published by the National Geographic Society, The Audubon Society, The National Wildlife Federation, and Field & Stream, Outdoor Life and Sports Afield magazines, among many others. Michael is an active member of NANPA (North American Nature Photography Association) and has served as president of that organization. Mike regularly leads photography trips throughout North American. Mike lives in Billings, Montana, with his wife, two daughters, and 15 turtles and tortoises. His photography may be seen at www.michaelfrancisphoto.com and www.agpix.com. His email is michaelfrancisphoto.com.

More books about bears from Riverbend Publishing

Hiking With Grizzlies: Lessons Learned By Tim Rubbert

This book uses photographs of the author's actual bear encounters to dramatically illustrate how to react safely if you meet a bear on the trail. Each encounter teaches important hiking strategies and gives hikers more confidence to enjoy bear country.

"If you are planning to hike through the wilderness, give this book a careful reading—it could very well save your life."—*Midwest Book Review*

"This book is like a first-aid manual for travel in bear country. It could be the best $10.95 you ever spend. After reading this book, you should gain new knowledge and confidence for your travels in bear country."
—*North American Bear Foundation*

Great Wyoming Bear Stories

By Tom Reed

The first-ever collection of the best bear tales from all across Wyoming, including Yellowstone and Grand Teton national parks. "An immensely valuable book for understanding and living with Wyoming's bears."—*Laramie Daily Boomerang*

Bears I Have Known

By Bob Murphy

A former park ranger relates his most memorable experiences with bears in Yellowstone and Glacier national parks. These first-hand stories are great entertainment and an inside look at early bear management in our national parks. "This is not your average bear book. It's a lifetime's experience in bear country."
—*Bozeman Daily Chronicle*

Great Montana Bear Stories

By Ben Long

Maulings, close calls, and even humorous escapades are all found in these stories, complete with discussions about how to hike, camp, and live safely in bear country. "A must-read for all lovers of wilderness." —*Missoulian*

THE HIGHLY PRAISED COMPANION BOOK TO *Yellowstone BEARS in the Wild*

Yellowstone WOLVES in the Wild

By Dr. James C. Halfpenny, Foreword by Dr. Douglas W. Smith

An unprecedented portrait of individual wolves and wolf packs, and how wolves are changing the park's very nature.

"The book is breathtaking! For anyone who has traveled to Yellowstone in recent years and seen the wolves, this book is must reading."
—*National Wildlife Federation*

"It's fabulous."—*Defenders of Wildlife*

"Captivating and thoroughly fascinating."—*Big Sky Journal*

"Photographically rich."—*Washington Post*

"Outstanding and very accurate. (Halfpenny) puts all the scientific research into common language. He filled in with personal observations. The stories really personalize what happened."—Ed Bangs, Wolf Recovery Coordinator, U.S. Fish & Wildlife Service

"A great collection of photographs and a compelling story."—*Jackson Hole News*

"Absolutely beautiful."—*Wolf Magazin, Germany*

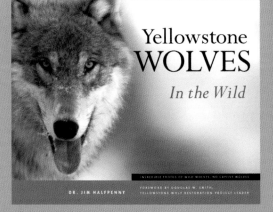